Summer in the Mitten

A collection of writings

by

Shiawassee Area Writers

Summit Street Publishing

SUMMER IN THE MITTEN
Published by Summit Street Publishing
131 West Grand River
Owosso, Michigan 48867

ISBN 978-1-7326522-4-8

Publishing in the United States by Summit Street Publishing, Owosso, Michigan.

Cover Art: Jim Edward Hill
Cover Design: Emily E. Lawson Photography

Printed in the United States of America
2020

10 9 8 7 6 5 4 3 2 1

The Shiawassee Area Writers started in May 2017 to help individuals have a gathering where interaction, collaboration, finding empathy as well as joy, could be found in the process of writing and publishing.

This is the third anthology for the Shiawassee Area Writers group. Their first anthology was published in September 2018 and entitled, *Winter in the Mitten.* In September 2019, the group published *Spring in the Mitten.*

Proceeds from this book will go toward local high school scholarships for seniors pursuing degrees or continued education in creative writing, literature, or journalism.

For more information, contact President/Founder Elizabeth Wehman at shiawasseeareawriters@gmail.com. Meetings are held twice a month, please visit www.shiareawriters.com for meeting dates and times.

"The Shiawassee Area Writers have taught me that writing, editing, and publishing does not have to be an isolated, head-banging, lonely process. It's a much more rewarding experience when you share your ideas, thoughts, strengths, and then receive honest feedback to make your stories the best they can be before releasing them into the world."

~ Patti Rae Fletcher

Since 2004, ***Patti Rae Fletcher*** has studied writing technique through college courses and conferences. Before her first book, *This Sign Was Mine, Message Received!,* she published articles and photographs in dozens of magazines. She presently is the Vice President of the Shiawassee Area Writers, a group established in 2017.

Her most recent book release is a children's creative non-fiction picture book, titled *Whoa Nilly a Nymph Grows Up!* It is about a dragonfly's lifecycle-incomplete metamorphosis which uniquely includes both illustrations and actual photos, along with amazing facts, and comprehensive questions. Book two in this series will be about the lifecycle of the Mexican jumping bean.

This Sign Was Mine, is an inspirational memoir and has received all five-star reviews. The sequel titled *Celebrate Your Life's Miracles* is in the process of final edits and should be released before Christmas 2020. The upcoming memoir is also about the unexplainable signs, synchronicities, divine interventions, and love from the Universe all in the most perfect timing and sometimes goes beyond all human understanding. Patti believes each of us is given ethereal life guidance throughout our lives and believes each person can interpret their own messages to help make their life happier, healthier, and more joyful, no matter what the earthly circumstances.

Patti lives in lower east Michigan with her husband. When she isn't writing or editing, she enjoys the company of family and friends along with being outdoors exploring nature.

For updates please follow Patti on her Facebook pages. This Sign Was Mine@pattiraefletcher or Whoa Nilly@anymphgrowsup. Her new website will be available in the near future.

Rollercoaster Rookie!

Yes! *All of those stretches, hanging upside down, and eating vegetables must have done the job.* Today will be extra special, my final farewell to *Kiddies Court* after five annual family trips to *Kings Castle Amusement Park*. Believe it or not, me, little Hannah, has grown tall enough to stand perfectly even with the florescent green forty-eight-inch height bar. It's the "Big Kid Rides," from now on. Wahoo! *I get to hang out with my older cousins and their friends.*

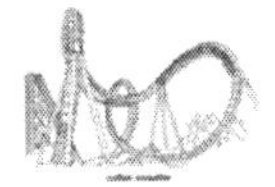

"Next. . .!" the ride operator yelled.

My twin cousins raced toward the first car of "The Squire's Scream."

"We get first car next time," Randy grumbled as we stepped into the second cart.

"I know you're bummed about your best friend not being able to come," I said, "but try not to let it ruin our day. We only get to come here once a year."

"Easy for you to say." Randy growled. "You're not stuck with a little girl cousin who has never ridden a coaster."

"I have too!" *Even though I knew the Caterpillar in Kiddie Court didn't count.*

"Okay kid, I'm warning you! Before my buddy Adeel came here with me, every partner I ever had got sick on coasters. Don't you dare hurl on me." Randy snarled, "Hear me—Rollercoaster Rookie?"

I gnawed on my lower lip and held back the tears as I nodded. Randy usually ignored me at family functions but was never mean. He liked to hang-out with the older boys. I hoped my dry mouth and jittery stomach were only nerves. *Click.* The lap bar locked! *No turning back now.* I sucked in a breath, squeezed my eyes shut, and gripped the rubber handle with both hands. *I can do this!*

Our cart lurched. An awful *ka-chunk, ka-chunk* filled the air. At a snail's pace, the chained rails carried us higher until we paused at the top. I peeked through my eyelashes. Randy raised his arms over his head. The wind caused my skin to feel like a too tight Halloween mask. We both screamed. My stomach hit my tonsils as we raced headfirst to the ground. We zipped around the last curve and jerked to a stop. My brain felt jumbled and not a drop of spit was left in my mouth. The buzzer rang. Randy nudged me. "It's over rookie, open your eyes. What did you think of a real coaster?"

I let out a slow breath. "Wow!" *I didn't throw up.*

"Let's see how well you do on the next one." He said, "It's faster."

We ran from one twisted high-rise monster to the next.

"Hurry!" Randy yelled, "The line is short for the Dungeon of Doom."

Overhead the weathered wooden beams creaked and swayed. "Phew, what stinks?"

"That's oil." Randy said, "They use it on the rails to prevent old carts from slipping off the edge." He chuckled and added,

"You're pale. This could be your return to Kiddies Court."

"Quit laughing, I'm fine." *Good thing he couldn't see my insides.* We stepped into a wobbly wooden boxcar. *Ka-chink.*

After being on coasters that shot backwards, hung upside down, and plunged us through total darkness, I had passed Randy's test. That was until I saw the coaster in front of us. "Is . . . that a cloud . . . resting on top. . .of the first hill?" I gulped. *Breathe.*

"We saved the best for last," Randy said. "It's new this year, the Three Headed Beast breaks all records for height, speed, and spinning, but I'm not scared."

I wondered what the record was for getting sick on this ride. We inched forward through the line maze. Spine chilling screams echoed as the Three Headed Beast carried its victims down steep hills and spun around sharp turns. The French fries I devoured earlier seemed to come alive, as I watched the terrified expressions on people's faces as they zoomed above us. I touched my stomach, *Stay in there. I can do this.*

The operator strapped us in cushioned cages, six in a line as we stood upright, and then once the extra padded bars locked over our heads, they tilted us back, so we faced the sky. This ride swung, twisted, and flipped over the center bar. *At least if I lose my fries they should go straight down.* I hoped.

We zigzagged around curves at a speed that caused my lips to stretch sideways. The ride paused at the highest point, leaving us upside-down to ponder our demise. When I saw what was coming next, my throat tightened, my heart raced, and my eyes closed. *I can do this, I repeated.* The Beast took us through a triple corkscrew. *I'm going to die.* "Ah," a sigh of relief escaped as the ride slowed. I laid my head back to catch my breath as we pulled into the exit, or at least that's what I thought. *Wrong.* The cage swung to the side and picked up speed. We swerved around two more corners for an unexpected deep dive through a dark scary cave before this Three Headed Beast came to an abrupt stop. I opened one eye, then the other. *I'm alive! I did it!* "Whoa, that was so . . . crazy! Let's go again."

Everyone agreed. We high-fived and returned to the line for our final ride before we had to meet-up with our parents. Anxiously waiting our turn, I noticed Randy's arms crossed over his stomach, his face pale and scrunched.

"You okay?" I asked.

He shook his head, waved us on, and ducked beneath the rails and ropes, through the people, and to the nearest trash can.

Randy waited on a bench for us at the ride exit.

"It's okay," I said as I patted his back. "You can be my Rollercoaster Rookie next year, just keep saying, "I can do this!"

"I deserved that," He said, chuckled and swung his arm over my shoulder. "You're alright for a girl and you proved you're not a Rollercoaster Rookie."

Patti's Bee and Bee

The sound of the swarm zapped my attention from my book to a dark shadow headed straight toward me. The buzz grew more intense with every second. As I hurried from my seat, in a panic, the back of chair bumped the screen door, knocking it off of its track. Somehow, I managed to slam it closed at the exact moment the bees arrived.

I remember as a child, Mom would squeal, her arms flailing whenever a bee came near. We'd do the bee dance all the way into the house. At some point she'd gotten braver, however I had not.

So, you can imagine my reaction as I sat on the deck, enjoying a comfy lounge chair, summer sunshine, and a new book when I was visited by thousands of uninvited bees. Before this incident, I thought this only happened in cartoons.

They didn't fly by as I expected. They buzzed, flew chaotically, and swirled around the deck and yard until they came to rest one by one on the underside of my cement birdbath about two feet from my window. My heart thumped louder than the buzz. I was alone and had no idea what to do.

I thought of my husband's torch, and a can of wasp spray in the shed. They both seemed worthless ammunition against so many bees. My life flashed before my eyes. They would attack and sting me from every angle. I could be stung to death, blanketed by bees. I shuddered.

I double and triple checked all the screens and made sure there were no rips. Once I felt safe, I allowed myself to observe the swarm's activities and quickly became enthralled with what they were doing and wondered why.

They clung to each other and created the formation of an upside-down living mountain. They piled on row by row. The mound appeared to be breathing, pulsing, and swaying as one. They harmonized perfectly. I became mesmerized by their interaction and connectedness.

Since my computer was near, I began a search. In the first few clicks I discovered my visitors were honeybees. The article suggested that I call a local beekeeper. They may want to add more bees to their collection. *What a relief.*

I found two bee hobbyists near my location and called. "Hello, are you interested in rescuing me, oops, I mean rescuing gazillions of bees that have taken over my birdbath?"

Before I could say anything more, the beekeeper replied in a hurried voice, "Whatever you do, please don't destroy them. Not many people get the opportunity to experience a new colony forming."

Oh boy, lucky me. "When can you come and get them?"

"I'm not in need of more bees. However, if you leave them alone, they will depart on their own in as little as two hours and maybe stay up to thirty, but I promise they will leave."

"Are you sure? They appear to be making themselves quite comfy here."

The beekeeper explained that when a colony becomes too large, it separates. The new queen can't fly long distances. When she tires, she lands, and all the bees surround her, covering her for her protection. Once they are settled, scout bees are sent out to locate a new permanent home for its queen and the new colony.

The next day while in the kitchen I recognized the chaotic buzz and hurried to the window. The bees dispersed the same way they had come. Layer by layer they dotted the air and flew west. Their visit lasted about twenty-two hours.

After the swarm left, I noticed several scout bees had returned to the birdbath. They discovered their queen and the new colony—gone. It was the first time I had ever felt sorry for bees. They hung around the birdbath for several days and appeared confused. I could only hope they would eventually rejoin their colony and new home.

Since learning a bit about the complex life of a honeybee, I have more respect, less fear, and with my adoration of honey, I now have a new appreciation of these bees.

They are welcome at my Bee and Bee anytime. (**Note:** Short term only)

The Almost Invisible Waterfalls

"Oh, and did I mention, there are only outhouses available at this campground." Two Mom's, five children. I reiterated, "There are no public showers and you have to pump your own water. Are you sure you want to do this for a long weekend?"

"Real camping," Ella said, "that's the best!"

Ella's daughters were the same age as my two sons and had known each other all their lives. At the time of this trip they were pre-teens with her youngest son being eight-years old.

By the time we had reached our destination, almost six hours in Ella's van, we wondered, "What had we been thinking?" However, the second we were out of the vehicle; we knew we had made the perfect choice.

We had plenty of chuckles hiking through the forest. The boys found an assortment of animal poop, and pointed it out to the girls, and were delighted to see their reactions. The kids had rowing and fishing contests along with great success in frog and snake hunting.

To me, there aren't many moments in life better than the sound of waves splashing against old steel boats, sunsets over rippled water, and the pop of sparks from the bonfire dancing beneath the stars. The sounds and scents of Mother Earth made it all worthwhile despite the lack of normal conveniences.

After two days, our box of wet wipes wasn't quite enough to quench the stank of all our camping experiences. We needed a bath.

Ella suggested we could explore a neat waterfall she had read about in a magazine. It wasn't too far from our campsite. She had copied the information and had it in her glove compartment.

"Are you serious," I asked, "a waterfall? I'm in!"

She said, "Yep, Ocqueoc (auk-we-auk) Falls. The article described them as being connected to seven lakes which spans over twenty miles, and they're not far from here."

We would pack a picnic, our suits, towels, and sunscreen in the morning, and go for a short road trip where perhaps we could bathe at a waterfall. The kids oohed and aahed in delight.

Waterfalls have always seemed magical to me. There are breathtaking falls in Michigan's Upper Peninsula; however, I had no idea there were any in lower Michigan, and less than an hour away. I hardly slept.

In the morning, after a quick stop at a Walmart to gather more snacks, we turned into a gravel parking lot.

My son said, "Wow, looks like we get the falls all to ourselves." There were no other cars in sight.

We put on sun and insect protection, then made our way to the edge of the woods. We headed in the direction the arrow-shaped plank sign pointed. In an instant, we felt moisture in the air. The slight breeze rustled the leaves, and the birds chattered above. Each of our steps caused tiny critters to scurry on the forest floor.

"Everyone, listen," Ella's youngest son said, his eyes widened, "I hear water." We picked up our pace in anticipation. "There it is," her son squealed. We paused at the opening in the woods and saw the rushing stream, but no waterfalls. We continued along slanted ground, fallen branches, and large gnarled tree roots. The air smelled of earthy moss and pine. The sounds of the water grew louder.

As the shaded path opened, I gasped at the rays of sun that glistened on the natural formation of the falls. To our surprise, the kids suddenly broke into hysterical laughter—bent over, holding their bellies. The comments went from one to the other. Layering on the sarcasm and ingratitude that only the pubescent could contrive.

"No way. These aren't real, more like invisible waterfalls."

"Waterfalls. These are puny."

"Yeah, sissy falls." The guffaws and comments continued.

"I thought they would be like Niagara Falls."

I agreed, Ocqueoc Falls were minuscule in comparison, but the sights and sounds and being surrounded by its splendor helped me to remember how magnificent the world is in which we live. The rushing pristine water, fresh forest scents, and even some remnants of an old mill race, above the falls, promised to make this day a phenomenal experience.

It didn't take long before the children's screeches of joy seemed to echo from all around. They slipped and slid across the shiny flat stones on their bottoms and over the different levels as the water pushed them into the natural pools beneath the falls. Here they splashed and did silly imitations of their mom's and how we told them about these spectacular falls. We enjoyed their exaggerated exchanges and chuckled. Their sarcastic teasing disappeared into pure laughter and imagination.

As I listened to the giggles and chattering from the kids, I reverently dipped my feet and hands in the water before I lowered myself onto a sun warmed colorful stone beneath the surface. I tried to envision our indigenous ancestors as they may have fetched water and dipped their toes at this very location.

As I entered this pure, sacred, and unsurpassed stream, I knew Ocqueoc Falls would be a part of me, my sons, and our friends' lives forever.

"Shiawassee Area Writers has captured the spirit of Motown—talented authors encouraging and promoting one another toward success. Just as Motown breathed a new sound, so S.A.W. is breathing new life into the written word. I am humbled and grateful to be surrounded by such talent and vision."

~ Laurie Salisbury

Laurie Salisbury lives in a rambling old farmhouse in the middle of Michigan. She is an author and a speaker. She has published four children's chapter books in the He Reigns series and is currently working on book five, *The Harness of the Lord.* Other publications include *Nothing to Fear*, an infant/toddler picture book based on II Timothy 1:7, and several short stories in two different anthology collections.

Laurie lives with her husband, Larry, and three of their children. Family pets include a small rescue dog of no particular breed, a Labradane, and a Russian tortoise. But Laurie's favorite pet is her distinguished feline friend, a fluffy tomcat named Dickens.

Laurie spent many years loving and serving children. She raised nine children, and gave a temporary home, love, and direction, to twenty-eight foster children. She also served in the Children's Ministry for over thirty years.

Find out more about Laurie at www.lauriesalisbury.com or join her on Facebook @lauriesalisburyauthor.

Hope in Him! Laurie Salisbury

When Hope Grows

The island brochure boasted beautiful vistas, shopping, and horse drawn carriage rides. Rylee had dreamed of a Mackinac Island vacation for years. Mason would love the sightseeing while she begged for more time near the water. With a tight budget, Rylee mapped out a plan that would make the most of every hour.

The phone beside her played a country tune and Mason's picture appeared on the screen.

"Hi, sweet stuff. What's up?" she answered.

"I got a call from the landlord." Mason did not sound happy.

"What does he want? I *paid* the rent."

"One of his kids wants to move into our house."

"He's kicking us out? Are you serious?" Rylee's chest tightened. "How much time is he giving us? He has to give us a month, right?"

"That's *all* he's giving us. We have to be out on June first."

Rylee could hear the strain in his voice. "We'll figure it out," she said, attempting to sound positive. "I got the newspaper today, I'll look for rentals."

"What are we going to find for two adults, six kids, and a dog?"

It was heart-wrenching to hear the worry in his tone. "We'll just have to pray about it. I'll check the paper. I gotta go, Em is trying to get out the back door again."

Rylee pressed end on her phone and ran to catch the two-year-old before she made it outside.

"Emberly Rose," she scolded. "Where are your toys?"

The brown-haired tot pointed toward the living room. "Put down," she said, kicking her pudgy legs.

"How about we go for a walk? She called to Emberly's twin brother. "Marshall, do you want to go for a walk?"

A smile lit up his chubby face. "Walk to cows!"

Rylee pulled her long dark hair into a ponytail and grinned at his excitement. "Yes, we'll go see the cows." She refused to allow worry to take hold and kept a cheerful demeanor. Moving would not concern the kids. It was her responsibility to make sure they saw it as an adventure.

The older four were just as agreeable to a walk as the twins. Rylee watched as they ran ahead while she pushed the double stroller. Keeping the busy toddlers contained left her mind free to focus on praying. *Father, we need your help.* The prayer started out okay, but quickly dissolved into all the frightening what-ifs. *What if we can't find a place? What if we have to move in with our parents? What if we have to give up our vacation? Snap out of it, Rylee. You'll find something.* She turned her attention to the joy and laughter of the kids in front of her. *'I'll think about that tomorrow.'* The Scarlett O'Hara quote from *Gone with the Wind* wasn't at all biblical, but at the moment, she thought it was good advice.

In a blink it seemed, two weeks had gone by with no available —within the budget, large enough for a family of eight—rental options. Mason's blue eyes had no sparkle today.

Rylee flinched at the thought of telling him about the offer she got earlier that morning. She bit her bottom lip. "Margot said we could stay with them until we find something."

Mason's face contorted. "Where?"

"She says they have a bedroom adjoining her attic. Her girls will double up, and we can sleep in the bedroom with the twins. She'll clean out the attic for our older four."

"Eleven kids in one house?" Mason rubbed the back of his neck.

"And four of them are two-year-olds. I know. But we don't have any other options right now."

"We might have one." Mason didn't look any happier about his option than he did about living with eleven kids. "A guy at work knows a realtor who might be able to find us a home that would qualify for an FHA loan."

"Can we do that? Can we afford a house? How much does a realtor charge?"

Mason shrugged and Rylee let the subject drop for the time being.

Living with Margot and her family turned out to be much less stressful and more organized than Rylee had imagined. The kids entertained each other on the hot summer days. With Margot and Mason working out dinners, Rylee had time to watch all the kids and run them to their various appointments and activities. In the evenings, Margot's husband, Jim, played hide and seek or tag with the kids. Occasionally, a bonfire followed.

Rylee weighed the news in her mind. The good news was the house: a beautiful four-bedroom, two-bath, with a gable front on a large lot. The bad news was two-fold: first, in order to qualify for the loan, they would have to fix the back steps and paint the exterior of the house. Second, the improvements would take a huge bite out of the vacation fund. Which meant the vacation would have to be on the mainland in historic Mackinaw City. There would be no carriage rides and more window shopping than actual shopping. On the other hand, homeownership was within sight and at least the vacation was still a possibility.

The brilliant sun reflected her mood on the drive to church. Rylee's heart swelled with thanksgiving. Margot and Jim had let them in on a surprise over the weekend. They had organized a group from church to paint the new house, which meant vacation packing had commenced. And today was a special day. There would be several baptisms and a picnic following the service. She had dropped Mason and eight-year-old Andrew, off at the park to take their turn tending the roast pig.

"Good morning, King family." The greeter was a kind middle-aged gentleman named Frank. He had a gentle manor and always carried mints in his pockets for the kids.

Rylee let the kids run off with their friends while she chatted with him.

"Any news on the new house?" he asked.

Marshall played nearby, and Rylee noted that Emberly had followed the big kids into the fellowship hall.

"The steps are finished and a painting day is scheduled for next Thursday."

"I'll be sure to put that on my calendar. Lynn and I both want to help. Can we bring any food for the crew?"

Rylee nodded and scanned the passing group of children hoping to see Emberly among them. "Did you hear that?" She strained to hear the sound again.

"It's probably just the kids playing," he smiled and brushed his hand at an imaginary worry.

"It sounded like one of them crying. I better go check."

It never ceased to amaze Rylee, when in an emergency, how the Holy Spirit would envelop her in his peace and give her wisdom. She could see the blood on Emberly's tiny face even through the glass door and assessed the situation as she moved toward the girls. Clare was holding Emberly's hand and didn't appear to notice the problem. Emberly toddled along behind neither crying nor screaming. Rylee pulled the door open. At that moment, one of the bigger boys caught sight of Emberly's face.

"She's bleeding!" His outburst got the attention of everyone in the room including a shocked Clare.

Clare's countenance fell as the color drained from her face. She dropped Emberly's hand as Rylee reached to pick the toddler up. She held the little girl in her arms and assessed the wound. Something had torn Emberly's eyelid nearly off.

Clare bolted for the restroom and Rylee's heart went out to her as the tender-hearted big sister ran to hide from the horror of the accident. Rylee scanned the room for another adult, hoping someone could comfort her oldest while she cared for Emberly. "Clare, don't go in there. That's where I'm going. Susan, can you help Clare?"

In the bathroom, Rylee sat Emberly on the counter to get a better look. The left eyelid was torn from the inner eye to the center of the lid, and now hung limp and jagged. Emberly's sweet brown eye peered at her mom through tiny blood caked lashes.

"That's going to need some stitches." Rylee smiled and spoke in a reassuring tone to the tiny tot. Thankfully, there was no gushing blood. And while the eye itself did not appear to be affected, Rylee made a note to keep watch and brace herself for what the doctor might say. It only took a few minutes to clean Emberly's face and apply a wet paper towel to the affected eyelid.

So many things ran through Rylee's mind as she carried the toddler back out into the hall that morning. *Thank you, Lord, for keeping Emberly calm. I have to get this kid to the hospital. I need help and a babysitter. Why is Clare sitting by herself and crying? Where is Susan?*

She spotted Susan with a group of women standing near a Sunday school room. "I need help."

"What do you need?" Sue's question felt oddly cold.

What do I need? Can't you see my baby? What do you mean, what do I need? Rylee took a deep breath.

"I need someone to keep my kids while I take this one to the hospital. And I need someone to come with me to help Emberly while I drive."

"You can leave the kids here, someone will watch them."

Sue's cool tone did not inspire the confidence that Rylee had hoped for, but she had to trust that her kids would be cared for. It hurt that none of the ladies volunteered to ride along to the hospital with her. She gathered the children, to let them know what was happening and reassured them that all would be well. To set her mind at ease, she signed the kids into their Sunday school classes and asked Clare to help watch the younger ones.

"What happened, Clare?" Rylee had to get more information to take to the hospital.

"I don't know." Tears filled her eyes. "I went to get her and I thought she just bumped her head on the grill over there."

The men's group had left a barbeque grill in the fellowship hall after their Saturday meeting. She would need to inspect it before she left to try and identify what actually happened.

The pools of tears in Clare's eyes tore at Rylee's heart. *She needs me right now as much as Em does.* "Don't worry about it, sweetheart. I think she just needs a few stitches." Rylee put her free arm around Clare's sagging shoulders and squeezed. "It's not your fault. Things happen. Look, she's not even crying. She's fine." Rylee was thankful that Emberly was taking the freak accident in stride, *and* that Clare's teacher arrived and immediately took over consoling and redirecting Clare.

As she and Emberly were on their way out, Margot opened the door. Rylee heaved a sigh of relief. "I don't have time to explain, please, watch my kids. I have to run to the hospital. To Rylee's great relief, Margot agreed.

As it goes with so many emergencies, Rylee's mind was so focused on getting Em to the hospital, she hadn't even given a thought to Mason until she pulled out of the church drive.

He's at the park! With the park on the way, it made sense to swing through and pick him up.

"She did what?" Mason ran to the driver's side door. "Move over. I'll drive."

Andrew hopped in the backseat beside Emberly offering her a good distraction.

"My best guess is that she caught her eyelid on the utensil hook when she walked past the grill. I don't think you need to drive this fast. It hasn't bled too much and she isn't complaining." Rylee secretly hoped there were no police on their route.

Mason glanced over his shoulder to check on Emberly. "I can't believe how good she's being."

At the hospital they met with their own physician who gave them some gauze and saline to keep the wound moist. "I am not going to attempt this. You need to take her to Sparrow Hospital. And do not let anyone but an ophthalmologist examine her."

After the initial check-in at the Lansing hospital, the chief of surgery was called.

"Let's get that stitched up." He said after a short examination.

"Are you an ophthalmologist?" Mason asked.

"No. Is that who you want?"

Another hour of waiting followed. A pleasant man showed up and sat in the chair beside Rylee. Emberly sat perfectly still on her lap as he gently lifted her eyelid and examined it with a magnifying glass. "Do you see this tiny dot?" he asked.

Rylee and Mason leaned in and nodded.

"That's the tear duct. I can go in and stitch her up but the tear duct will give her a problem for the rest of her life. I recommend that you take her to University of Michigan Hospital. They have specialists who can help her. I'd offer you an ambulance, but she looks like she's more comfortable with you."

Two hours away, another hospital, more waiting and more doctors. Rylee was exhausted. It was all so surreal. *How did we get here, God?* She pictured the vacation brochure that was tucked in her purse. *It seems like yesterday we were planning a summer vacation.*

Emberly sat content on her lap as more doctors examined her eyelid and consulted with each other in whispers.

"We've called Doctor Ezekiel Altman. He's flying in from Minnesota. He has the microsurgical skills needed for your daughter's reconstruction."

"Minnesota? What time will he get here?" Rylee glanced at the clock that read quarter past eight.

"He is en route. Surgery is scheduled for ten-thirty. Follow me. We'll get the prep work done before he gets here."

Two hours later, Rylee watched as Dr. Altman carried her baby off to surgery.

"Mason."

He put his arms around her and squeezed as pent emotions found their release.

Summer slipped away that year without the usual gaiety. The kids were enrolled in their new school and they would move into the new house next week. The shock and fear from that horrific day, along with the memory of Susan's coldness, had softened with time. Seeds of hope sprouted once again and forgiveness had its way in her heart.

It wasn't Mackinac Island or even Mackinaw City, but a day trip to Lake Michigan was just what Rylee needed. "Only up to your belly button," Rylee cautioned as Marshall waded deeper into the water.

"Fish!" He squealed and pointed to the minnows gathering around his feet.

With Mason occupying the older children in the deeper water with a raucous game of tag, Rylee focused on the twins. "Don't splash, Em, we can't get your eye patch wet. Do you want to build a castle with Mama?" Rylee handed a pail to her brave little girl. *She never cried. All that day with no food or water. Doctors poking and prodding. Who will you be— my strong, amazing, sweet baby girl?*

Jackson Pollok Jackson Pollok

"I've loved writing for many years. When I was seven years old, I began writing and illustrating my own books. My favorite part of writing is using my imagination. I write pages and pages without slowing down. Writing is a great way to express what you're thinking. I use writing to plan my YouTube videos. I take notes, create storyboards and then film the videos.

As I got older, I wanted to learn how to get a story in a book. In the ninth grade, I joined the Shiawassee Area Writers, and I'm excited to have a story published. I've learned extra writing details like point of view, italics, punctuation, and making better word choices. It's also great to be a member because every member makes each other feel welcome and we stick up for one another. It's nice because everyone is good at something different, and we all learn from each other's writings."

~Jackson Pollok

Jackson Pollok is a fifteen-year-old who lives with his family on a farm in Shiawassee County. Jackson joined the Shiawassee Area Writers in 2019 at the encouragement of his homeschool teacher, Shawn Gallagher. This is his first published story.

Jackson especially enjoys writing adventure stories and comedies for his YouTube channel, JBP500, which has over 3,000 subscribers and over 1.3 million viewers. He is also an athlete, nature enthusiast, prankster and ukulele player. He wants his writing to inspire people and make them laugh.

Shawn Gallagher

"I learned of the Shiawassee Area Writers when I visited their booth at the county fair. They were enthusiastic about their mission to support writers of all abilities and interests and so encouraging about giving their group a try, that I decided to attend a meeting. Now, three years later, I have published pieces in three of the group's short story collections.

We are given the freedom to write in whichever genre we choose, including memoirs, fiction, horror, nature and poetry. This year, I attempted something I've wanted to do for many years. I collaborated with one of my homeschool students, Jackson Pollok, to write a fictional tale for "Summer in the Mitten." We worked for months outlining, writing, editing and revising our story. We both participated in SAW monthly meetings so we could both broaden our skills and sharpen our story. Jackson has received a priceless education in writing that goes beyond a typical school curriculum.

I will be forever grateful to SAW for this opportunity to have a lasting memory of our time together as teacher and student. The Shiawassee Area Writers is a welcoming association of people with diverse interests and backgrounds. One of my favorite parts of the meetings is when folks share a piece they are working on and receive feedback from their fellow writers. I would like to offer the same advice I received to anyone with an interest in writing—give the group a try." ~Shawn Gallagher

Shawn Gallagher is a retired special education teacher who now works with homeschool and afterschool students. She especially enjoys engaging them in the creative writing process, whether through narrative tales, poems, song lyrics or memoirs. She feels very fortunate to be able to share her enjoyment of writing with young people. Although more of a hobby writer, Shawn is pleased to have stories published in all three of the Shiawassee Area Writers anthologies. Her "Summer in the Mitten" tale is her first teacher/student collaboration.

Enjoy!
Shawn Gallagher

The Long Road Home

Everything in Ricky's world was about to change. He walked away from the funeral service speechless and traumatized. Head down, hands in his pockets, he struggled to hold back tears. This was the worst week of his fifteen-year-old life. The loss of both parents in a head-on car crash left him feeling devastated and hopeless. Through damp eyes, he saw his Aunt Linda approaching. She was his mom's older sister. Ricky's parents adored her, but he'd only met her a few times. She'd moved west in her twenties, drawn by the mountains and canyons she loved.

Her home would be his home soon. It was nearly two thousand miles away in Tucson, Arizona. He couldn't process all of the changes that lie ahead. Aunt Linda was fifty years old, too old to be a first-time mom, and she wasn't married. *What were his parents thinking when they named her his guardian?* Ricky couldn't bear the thought of everything he was leaving behind—his house, his friends, and most of all, his baseball team. It was early June, and their first game was to be played this week. A girl he'd had a crush on forever had said she'd be there. Taking a final look at the headstone engraved *Beloved Parents*, Ricky stopped in place to keep his knees from buckling. He didn't notice Aunt Linda waiting quietly for him. He was too overwhelmed with fear about his future and grief over the loss of Mom and Dad.

"This is my trusty camper van. More space than a car. There are a couple of benches for beds, a fridge, and a USB port for charging your electronics."

Ricky nodded. It looked pretty small. He spotted a camping stove, tent, air mattress and some fishing gear over the beds.

Aunt Linda followed his gaze and added, "It's about a thirty-hour drive, but I figure we can take it slow and use the time to get reacquainted. We can camp along the way home. We'll be passing through some interesting places. If we plan some stops, it will break up the drive." She waited hopefully.

She's making this sound like a vacation, Ricky seethed. *And my home is Michigan, not Arizona.* He picked at his fingernails. "Where's the bathroom in this thing?" He slumped into the passenger seat and stared out the window.

"We'll have to make stops for that." Her hopeful smile faded as she slid into her captain's chair and started the van. His lack of interest stung her. *Give him time,* she thought.

The first day, they drove from Lansing, Michigan to Springfield, Illinois. They were exhausted from packing Ricky's belongings and enduring the strain of the funeral.

"I reserved a spot in a campground not far ahead," Aunt Linda reported. "I stayed there a few times on my way to visit your family." It was nearly ten at night when they arrived and found their site.

"Whew, I'm beat," she announced, "How about you?"

Ricky inspected the cramped surroundings. *Where was he going to change? Not in front of Aunt Linda, that was for sure.*

"I'll hang this sheet in the back. We can take turns dressing," Aunt Linda offered. She appeared a few minutes later in pajamas covered with grinning frogs.

Ricky let out a heavy sigh. He didn't wear pajamas but said nothing. He slipped behind the makeshift curtain, quickly took off his shoes and socks and jumped fully-clothed into one of the beds. Pulling a blanket over himself and adjusting the pillow, he muttered, "Okay, ready." *This was so awkward.* Aunt Linda climbed into the bed across from his.

"Night, Rick."

"Yeah," was his muffled reply. He fell asleep to the howl of distant coyotes.

Ricky woke with a start in the middle of the night. *What was that noise?* He covered his head with his sheet and peeked toward Aunt Linda. She was snoring softly. A crinkling of paper was followed by a slammed cupboard door. *Was this a dream?* Out of the corner of his eye, he noticed the van door was slightly ajar. Someone was inside the camper.

"Aunt Linda, there's someone in the van," he whispered. She

tugged on her covers and rolled over. "Aunt Linda!" His voice grew louder as he saw one of the captain's chairs move. She bolted upright. "Listen," he cautioned.

Ricky reached up and grabbed a fishing pole. Aunt Linda wielded a long-handled flashlight. She aimed its beam toward the front of the vehicle. A pile of torn bags and food crumbs lay on the floor. A sudden movement caused the seat to spin, and a dark shadow materialized. Aunt Linda's hands trembled as she raised the light toward the culprit's face.

A large, wide-eyed raccoon sat in the swivel chair, crumbs falling from his whiskers as he clutched a bag of windmill cookies on his pudgy lap.

"Get out, you little thief!" Aunt Linda's voice shook and rose to a shriek.

Undeterred, the raccoon held the bag protectively and hissed. That did it. Ricky sprang from the bed. He swung the fishing pole at the raccoon and held the camper door open with his other hand.

"Beat it!" he ordered in his fiercest voice.

The raccoon tumbled from his seat, pausing to look toward his stash. Ricky tapped its fat behind with the pole, and it scurried into the night. He flashed a proud smile when he saw Aunt Linda's relieved face.

"Wow, Ricky. I'm glad you knew what to do. What a night. We better get back to sleep—or would you like a windmill cookie first?" They both laughed.

The next morning, Ricky was groggy from having his sleep interrupted by the raccoon, and his mood had changed. He'd dreamt of being at the zoo with his parents. He'd been about five or six and had walked between them, holding their hands. It was such a great dream. He'd loved feeding the giraffes and watching the playful otters swimming in their enclosure.

When he awoke, it was with the warm, secure feeling he always had when the three of them spent a day together. Gradually, the reality of his loss crept into his consciousness. A black cloud enveloped him. He shuffled outside where Aunt Linda was cooking breakfast over the camping stove.

She noticed his downcast face. "Good morning. Hey, I have an idea. Since we're in Springfield, how about taking time to see where Abraham Lincoln and his family lived before he became president? His home and presidential museum are both in town."

"Whatever." Ricky didn't care about a dumb old house and museum, but Aunt Linda might wander around and he'd have some time to himself. He was growing tired of being stuck with her.

After a few hours of exploring Springfield—which turned out to be not so bad after all—they returned to the van. Their next stop was Wichita, Kansas.

"Why don't we get a hotel tonight? We can both use it after the raccoon fiasco. You'll have a more comfortable bed, a hot shower, and a television to watch," Aunt Linda suggested.

"Sounds good to me." *Maybe I'll get my own room and be able to call some friends back home in private.*

Several hours later, they reached Wichita. Aunt Linda had tried to start conversations with Ricky, but he wanted no part of it. It seemed to him that she never stopped jabbering. He was irritated by her and by the radio news station she always kept on in the background.

Suddenly, something caught her eye. A pile of junk sat stacked by the side of the road, the unsold remnants of a recent garage sale.

"It's a picnic basket, just like the one my mom had! Can you believe someone is throwing it out?"

I sure can, mused Ricky.

"I'm going to grab it." Aunt Linda hopped from the van and headed toward the stack.

As Ricky watched, he saw a bit of something black, white and furry sticking out of the basket. He should probably warn her, but this might get interesting. He observed Aunt Linda walk with care through the cast-offs wearing a huge smile. She looked so darned excited about that silly basket. Maybe she missed Grandma. Ricky began to feel guilty.

"Wait!" he yelled, but it was too late. As she lifted the lid, she was met with a raised tail and a blast of putrid spray, delivered at point-blank range. Squealing in horror, she dropped the basket and tripped over a roll of discarded carpet. Ricky tried to squelch a grin as he watched the critter disappear along a ditch.

"I'm coated with it!" she exclaimed as she returned to the van. "I can't believe I didn't see the skunk. There must have been leftover food in the basket. What a nightmare."

Ricky inhaled a rank scent as Aunt Linda climbed inside. It enveloped everything, including him. "Oh man, you stink, Aunt Linda." He gagged and choked as his eyes burned and watered.

"Hate to tell you, but now so do you. I see a convenience store ahead. I'm going to drop you there. Get some peroxide, baking soda, and Dawn dish soap. The sooner we wash this smell off, the better."

"What? Why don't you go inside? You're the one who got sprayed."

"Because I smell worse than you. Here's the money. Go on now."

He had never felt so humiliated. As he searched for the items, he noticed several people pinch their noses and giggle behind their hands. They were staring at him.

"Whoa there, pal. Have a little run-in with a skunk?" the clerk asked in a loud voice. "Maybe I should hose you off outside." Chuckles could be heard throughout the store, including from a group of girls his age. Ricky threw the money on the counter and stalked out. This was all Aunt Linda's fault. He fumed silently all the way to the motel. Once again, she sent him to retrieve the room key. The desk clerk leaned back with a scowl and, with reluctance, handed it to him.

After his shower, Ricky's nerves were still frayed. This was the most awful trip ever. He felt like crying as he plunked down on his bed.

"Glad that's over." Aunt Linda rubbed her wet hair with a towel. "I thought we could watch a baseball game. The Tigers are playing tonight. We can order in for dinner. What would you like? Pizza? Tacos? Burgers?

"Don't care."

"Okay, pizza. Let's see, topping choices are ground beef, chicken, mushrooms, green peppers. . ." she read from a card on the table.

"I said I don't care! I'm not hungry, and I don't want to watch the game. I only watch games with my dad." He trembled with fury.

"Ricky, please don't shout. I'm just trying to help. I understand how you feel."

"No, you don't. I've lost everything. I don't want to go camping or visit Abraham Lincoln's house, and I sure don't want to live with you in Arizona."

"Ricky, your life isn't over," she pleaded.

"Yes it is. You just don't get it," his voice cracked.

Aunt Linda was terribly hurt, but she tried to be understanding. "I'm so sorry. I know you're sad, and you have a right to be." She walked over and tried to hug him.

"Leave me alone. I don't need you or anyone else." He grabbed his jacket and the keys to the van. "I'm sleeping by myself tonight."

Peeking out the motel window from behind the curtain, Aunt Linda watched him kick furiously at the gravel in the parking lot as he headed for the van. She hoped he remembered to lock the doors.

The next morning, she grabbed their bags and headed for the camper. Ricky was already in his seat. She decided to give him time to himself on the twelve-hour drive to Mesa Verde, Colorado, which was their next stop. He looked hollow-eyed and broken as he bobbed his head to his music. His silence made her feel lonely and a complete failure as a guardian. She had a special outing planned for them. If this didn't work, she didn't know what she would do.

"Where are we?" Ricky asked as they came to a halt.

"Mesa Verde National Park in Colorado. I thought you might like to stretch your legs on the hiking trails. We're eight or nine hours from Tucson. We'll be home before long."

"Your home, not mine."

"Let's just get some sleep, okay? I'm too tired to discuss this with you right now. It looks like rain. We'll sleep in the van tonight."

"I'd be happier in the tent." Ricky grabbed the supplies and flew out the door.

"Suit yourself," she called after him. She'd had enough of his attitude.

Ricky struggled to assemble the tent and bed, but he would sleep on the ground before asking for help. Climbing into the lopsided shelter, he flopped down on the air mattress, put on his headphones and drifted off.

When Aunt Linda opened her eyes, she was surprised to see daylight. As she made coffee, she opened the tattered curtains over the window. Although she hadn't heard the rain overnight, massive puddles covered the ground and surrounded the tent. She pulled on her rubber boots and slogged through the mud to wake Ricky.

"Ricky!" she called, peering through a screened opening. There he was, sound asleep on the mattress, floating on a pool of muddy water like a castaway on a life raft. The tent was sloped to one side, and the rainwater had seeped in to fill a large depression beneath him.

"Oh my," she snickered. She shook the tent and called him again. The sound of a splash was followed by a loud shout.

"Hey. What the heck? My iPod and headphones are ruined!" He unzipped the canvas and came out, drenched with water.

"If you needed help, you could've asked." Aunt Linda tried to keep a serious expression.

"It's not funny," Ricky fumed. He knew he should've listened when she warned him about the rain, and this made him even angrier. Off he charged, enraged and embarrassed, while Aunt Linda disassembled the pathetic lodging.

He reappeared a while later in dry clothing and sturdy shoes, his mood a bit lighter. He would never tell Aunt Linda, but he was excited about the hike. He and his dad often studied maps of the national parks in the hopes of taking a family vacation to one. Mesa Verde was a favorite of theirs.

"I want to walk by myself," he stated quietly.

Aunt Linda noticed the binoculars around his neck. She knew they were a recent birthday gift from his parents. "Stay within earshot, and carry this with you." She tossed him a whistle. "If you hear mine, please answer right away with yours." Ricky nodded and sprinted ahead.

Aunt Linda was awed by the wildlife she spotted—mule deer, wild turkeys, and even a great horned owl. Views of ancient sandstone Pueblo cliff dwellings, for which the park was known, took her breath away. She wished that she and Ricky could take a ranger-led tour. *Next time,* she thought. Realizing she had lost track of time, she peered at her watch and was surprised to see that two hours had passed. *When had she last seen Ricky?* She whistled for him. No answer. Trying again and getting no response, she grew concerned.

Ricky paid little attention to the trail markers. Lost in thought and enjoying the scenery, he suddenly sensed an unusual stillness. He froze in place, afraid to turn around. With his heart lurching and eyes wide open, he scanned his surroundings.

His worst fears were confirmed; something was watching him. Not one hundred feet away stood a mountain lion, its head lowered and its stare fixed on Ricky. He tried to avoid panic, but his mind raced in terror. *What were you supposed to do in a situation like this?* The lion took a step toward him. *It's over,* he thought miserably. Expecting a mauling and praying it would be a quick one, he felt a pocket for his Swiss army knife and instead discovered Aunt Linda's whistle. With nothing to lose, he raised it to his quivering lips and blew.

By now Aunt Linda had drawn the attention of a nearby park ranger. "Heard your whistle, ma'am, Is there something wrong?"

"It's my nephew. He's a little inexperienced on trails, and he's not answering my signal. I'm worried he may be lost."

"Hop in my jeep. We'll cover more ground that way." As they bumped along, Aunt Linda noticed a rifle in the back and shuddered.

"He could've taken any of these trails." She tried the whistle again and was surprised to hear a faint whistle in return.

"It came from over there," the ranger indicated. Grabbing his rifle, he jumped down. "It's easier on foot from here."

Hearing the shrill sound of the whistle, the lion took a step backward, crouched down and growled at Ricky. He shook from head to toe and wondered how it would feel to die. *Would it hurt? Would he see his parents again?* At that moment, he knew Aunt Linda was right. His life wasn't over yet, and he didn't want it to be. He wanted to live. He wanted a future.

"Click-click." The large feline fell to the ground. A blue dart protruded from its side.

"You okay, young man?" The ranger rushed over to him. "You're a lucky guy. Lion sightings are rare, but they do happen. Making a noise with your whistle made you seem more powerful. It probably saved you. This cat's asleep for now—tranquilized. When my back-up arrives, we'll take it for observation, then relocation.

The support vehicles soon appeared, and Aunt Linda and Ricky rode in the jeep back to the van. Thanking the ranger profusely, they climbed into the camper to begin the final stretch of the drive to Tucson.

"Aunt Linda?"

"Yes?"

"I . . . uh . . . I think I should apologize for causing so much trouble. And I'm sorry I've been rude to you. It just hurts so much to lose Mom and Dad. It feels like a bad dream and I'll wake up and everything will go back to normal."

"Oh Ricky, I'm just so glad you are alive. I couldn't bear losing both your parents and you. I loved them a great deal, and I love you that much, too." She began to cry. "You've had a terribly painful loss. It must feel like you'll never be happy again. He nodded.

"Trust me, this will hurt for a very long time, but slowly the sharp edges of pain will soften. You'll always miss your parents, but there are people who will help you through this. I'd like to be one of them if you'll let me. And I promise to try to give you space when you need it."

Ricky let his tears fall freely. She did understand after all. He looked at her with eyes that acknowledged their shared heartache. She was, after all, family. He reached over and took her hand, holding onto it tightly.

"I have enjoyed learning to write better stories by being in the Shiawassee Area Writers group. There are some fine folks in the group and they encourage me to do better and learn more about proper writing techniques. I just plain like them and we like to celebrate our successes and failures in writing."

~ Cyndy Habermehl

Cyndy Habermehl is a graduate of Baker College, Owosso, with an Associates of Applied Science Degree. After thirty years working in the medical field, Cyndy is now enjoying her retirement years by writing memoirs, poetry and children's books. She lives with her husband, Lee, and they both live near the farm she grew up on, also where these stories originated. Cyndy has published her stories in the Shiawassee Area Writers works of Winter in the Mitten and Spring in the Mitten.

A Lesson in Trust

As I grew up, I often found myself in the school of hard knocks. One painful lesson I learned from my mother was trust. My parents had instructed me to stay at school all day and not walk downtown Durand at lunchtime. Some students did walk downtown from school to buy candy and other items at the Ben Franklin Store. Summer vacation was a couple of days away, and as I felt I was in the last days of junior high, and as I was going to high school next fall, I felt I was old enough to go. I went with my friends, Wanda and Mindy, to the Ben Franklin Store. They convinced me that my parents wouldn't even know, so just do it. The rule to not go downtown was given when I started at the junior high, and my parents trusted that I would obey it and would stay safe on the school grounds.

That evening, the very day I went downtown with my friends, when we had eaten supper, my mother and I were doing dishes. We had been talking about the day when my mother asked me, "What did you do for lunch today?"

As I was thinking that was a curious question, I answered, "I ate my lunch at school as I always do."

She paused. She looked at me and calmly said, "Were you at the Ben Franklin Store today at lunchtime?" I told her that I had not been there.

I said, "I know that you do not want me downtown at lunch."

Mother was very calm and collected. She placed the dish cloth on the countertop and began to walk toward the telephone on the wall. She asked me point blank, "If I should call Aunt Clover and ask her if she saw you in the Ben Franklin today, should I believe her or you?" She told me that Aunt Clover had been in the bank today, where mother was a teller, and had told mom that she had seen me there. She said, "It's your word against Aunt Clover's word."

Sheepishly, I hung my head and began to cry. I said, "Don't call her, mother, I have lied to you, I was there. I went against your wishes."

Mother did not ground me. She did not yell. She looked me in the eyes and said in a soft, controlled voice, "You have broken the trust we have between us. Trust is earned, and we have had a trusting relationship. But, when trust is broken, it takes time to rebuild it." She told me that from now on she will doubt things I say to her.

I think it would have been easier to take a spanking or be grounded, but no, this hurt me to the core. I never forgot this lesson and I have sought through life to keep our trust intact.

Visits with Great Grandfather Bruno

My great grandfather was an interesting man. As he was an amputee, he walked around on a pair of old wooden crutches. He wore old blue jean overalls and a dark green shirt. The overalls were his standard outfit. The trouser leg of the overalls that covered the below-knee amputation was held up and pinned in place by a large safety pin. He had a large build and he rarely smiled.

He never called me by my nickname, Cyndy. I was called Cynthia, my given name. When he would talk to me, he would speak to me in a gruff tone, as a school teacher. He had been a school teacher in the old Newburg School, just down the road from the house he lived in.

One winter day, he and my father were felling trees on the farm woodlot. A tree fell the wrong direction and landed on his leg, pinning him there while my father ran for help. After a few surgeries, it was decided the lower leg could not be saved and the decision was made to amputate below the knee.

On warm summer days, he would sit outside on the big stone porch at the old farm down the road. Great Grandma would often bring him an old metal wash basin and have him peel potatoes or apples for dinner. He had a small paring knife and I still don't know how he could do it, but he did a continuous peeling, without breaking it off. One time when I asked him how he did it, he would just say, "Oh, it's easy to do."

To this day, I myself have never been able to do a continuous peel.

As he would sit and peel, working on the chore at hand, he would challenge me by saying, "Cynthia, spell 'perpendicular'."

At that time, I was about in the third grade and I would say, "Great grandfather, I can't spell a big word like that."

He would say, "Why sure you can, sound the word out. What does it start with?"

I would say, a 'P' and he would say, "That's correct." Then he would say, "What is the next sound?"

I would say 'ER' and we would continue on with the lesson.

The time just seemed to fly by. Learning to spell words with him was great fun and I enjoyed it. Eventually, I learned to spell some pretty big words. Later in my adult life, as I worked as a Medical Transcriptionist, I appreciated all the tools of spelling he taught me. Our time spent together and memories made were a great blessing.

"I have been a member of Shiawassee Area Writers (SAW) since 2016. Over the years, I've learned about writing and publishing. I continue to learn. The people in this group are generous and a delight to be with. My work has been enhanced by their input. They are a supportive group, ready to help wherever they can. Many are hard workers committed to their craft. As serious as they are, they can be a lot of fun." L.K.Perry

L.K.Perry currently lives in Swartz Creek, Michigan where she grew up. Perry moved back to her childhood city in 2014 to help her brother take care of their aging mother. She has three granddaughters with a great-granddaughter due to arrive in the fall.

Inspired and encouraged by her family, Perry prefers to write memoirs. *Evergreen* in the anthology *Winter in the Mitten* compiled by Shiawassee Area Writers (SAW) is Perry's first published memoir. She contributed to SAW's *Spring in the Mitten* with three stories and plans to have a piece in the Autumn anthology, too.

Perry has been a member of SAW for four years. She has an Associate Degree in Liberal Arts received with honors, Phi Theta Kappa. Her studies included Literature, Poetry, Creative Writing, and Language. You can find more writings by this author at lkperry.com and readers may email her there.

Linden Tree

My mother has always loved trees. I guess I did too, but I never gave it much thought. We had four big maple trees in the backyard that I loved to climb. My grandparents lived on a farm with a lane that led to the woods. Grandma would take me there to search for wildflowers. In her front yard, a big oak stood with a tire swing, which could be fun when my sister pushed me high; and a great place to reflect when on my own. As I grew older, I began to appreciate trees for their beauty, strength, and comfort. God brought the Linden tree to my attention when I needed it most.

I moved to Grand Rapids in the late nineties to be near my granddaughters. Grand Rapids had beautiful homes accented by their landscapes with a variety of trees. Among the Red Horse Chestnut, Japanese Lilac, Gingko, and Tulip Tree, the Greenspire Linden caught my eye. The shiny heart-shaped leaves filled the branches with clusters of fragrant yellow flowers. Its beauty lifted my spirit. It was the summer of 2004 and I needed a spirit boost. Work had me stressed. I needed time off to be a caregiver for my sister. She had a long battle with cancer.

I had no vacation, personal, or sick time left. When I asked for time off to travel with my sister, Sherri, my supervisor said, "No. You need to think of yourself and let your sister go on her own."

I couldn't let her go alone. Why couldn't my boss understand? It was clear to me that I would be fired if I missed a week of unapproved time. I took a day to think about it. I had some money saved that I could get by on. I called my supervisor back.

My father passed away in 1963, and my mother remarried within a year. I had an older sister that had moved out and a younger brother at home. A year after my mom's second marriage, she had my sister, Sherri. My parents expected me to watch her for free. At fifteen, I had been babysitting other people's children since I was ten. I loved the money but often didn't enjoy the kids. I had decided I would never, ever have children of my own. No way!

Sherri, a colicky baby, cried all the time. Born premature, Sherri weighed five pounds at birth. She stayed in the hospital a week after mom came home. The tiny, red, skinny baby did nothing for me. I thought she was homely. She reminded me of the guy in the Lay's Potato Chip commercial with the big nose.

Sherri's appearance and disposition changed as she grew. Her complexion turned rosy as her face filled out, which made her nose a perfect fit. Curly, strawberry blonde hair shined along with her sunny personality. I thought her to be very cute.

Around five months old, I bonded with her. By the age of three, she had become my little buddy. We shopped for pretty clothes that matched her beautiful hair. She loved to twirl in front of the mirror.

Sherri discovered that she loved to make my brother and me laugh. She shuddered the first time she tasted a pickle. Of course, we laughed. She ate more pickles to get more giggles from us. She got the hang of puckering up her face and shaking her body so good that she could do it on command. We would say, "Sherri make us laugh," and she would.

Our stepfather loved to drive all over Michigan. We camped often. One of my first memories, we camped at Bay City State Park. We celebrated my birthday, which is on the thirty-first of May. We arrived at night and somehow pitched our tent on a low-sloped hill. I slept with my head down and woke with a headache. Not only that, but the temperature dropped below freezing. An uncle, aunt, and cousins camped with us. My aunt couldn't stop laughing about me sleeping upside down. It's a birthday; I'll never forget.

As Sherri got older, she didn't appreciate being bossed by her siblings. Sometimes we would ignore her when we had friends around, and she didn't like that either. When I had my first child, a distressed Sherri didn't like to share the spotlight. My daughter, Lisa, stole our mother's attention from her. Bad enough for Sherri that I noticed her less. Mom took care of Lisa while I worked. Five years difference in the girl's ages, they were more like sisters.

I have fond memories of us spending time with extended family members. My aunts and uncles owned a cottage near Higgins Lake. On Fourth of July holidays, we would take the boat or pontoon out on the lake to watch the fireworks. I loved floating on the water as the lights launched from a distant shore. The display of lights reflected on the water. The tiny-tots in their pjs had their comfy blankets and sippy cups.

Sherri grew into a fine young woman. At eighteen, she got married on Valentine's Day. Her husband, Paul, enlisted in the army and was stationed in Germany. He flew over first to get settled.

When it was time for her to join Paul, I took her to the airport. Not only was it her first time to fly, but she would be alone. She seemed worried. I wanted to reassure her. With a hug and a smile, I said, "I can't believe you get to see Germany. I wish I was going with you. I'm so envious."

Sherri loved Germany. Our mom visited her there. When Paul's deployment ended, she didn't want to come home. When she did return, I hardly recognized her. Her thin body had curves, and she moved with a new confidence.

Once home, Sherri met up with her old school chums, and she made new friends. You couldn't go anywhere with her without running into one of her friends. Often, she would make a new friend while we would be out and about. She loved people, and they loved her back. Sherri was the friendliest, most outgoing person in our family.

I didn't think she would ever have children. After nine years of marriage, Sherri became pregnant. In 1994 she gave birth to a beautiful baby boy. Born on the third of July, our family called him, our little firecracker. She named him Frank after her father, who had passed away when she was nine. It had been twenty- four years since we had a baby in the family. Frank lit up our world.

Two years later, my daughter Lisa had her first child and named her Elizabeth. Two years after Elizabeth, my daughter had Amanda in the spring; and Sherri had Mitchell in the fall. A second son to love. She called him her little sweet pea. She was overjoyed to have a brother for Frank. Our family grew, and we spent more time together. Fourth of July celebrations in Michigan were our favorite summertime events.

In 1999, six months after Mitchell's birth, Sherri discovered a lump in her right breast. The doctors thought it was nothing to worry about because of her young age. She insisted on a biopsy. It turned out to be a malignant tumor. The cancer was rare and fast-growing. She had to have her breast removed. This news devastated us. She would be only thirty-three years old in a month. We still celebrated a quiet Independence Day at her home.

In July 2002, her cancer had metastasized to her brain. It made her dizzy and nauseous. She could no longer work at the local pharmacy. She never complained or asked why. She still went to the school to help out in Frank's classroom. She would be so sick, but she pushed herself to do what she could.

On the fourth, we celebrated at Sherri's house. Paul cooked us a fabulous meal outdoors on the grill. The kids splashed in kiddie pools. A simple, relaxing holiday was just what we needed. When evening came, we relaxed on Sherri's deck and watched fireworks.

It seemed like every summer since her diagnosis; we would get more bad news. She searched for a new medical facility. Her current place couldn't help her anymore. All the treatment places she found required money she didn't have, and she would need to travel. My daughter and son-in-law, with family and friends, organized a golf outing and raised five thousand dollars for her. Sherri had a blast at the outing. People took turns driving her around the course in a golf cart.

After the fundraiser, Sherri could afford to travel to Cancer Treatments of America in Illinois. Some of her friends went with her when she had treatments to support her. Paul had to work to support the family and couldn't go with her. Our mother stayed with Frank and Mitchell while their dad worked. As time went on, her friends felt the strain on their own lives so I began to travel with her more.

In July of 2003, Sherri seemed to decline. I was apprehensive about celebrating, taking her out. That year our family took the kids, Sherri's sons and my granddaughters, to Yogi Bear Park near Frankenmuth. I had to go to the store to get ice. I told everyone to keep an eye on Sherri. When I got back, I saw her in a lawn chair all alone. I lost it. She was fine.

Later in the day, Sherri snuggled with Mitchell in front of the bonfire. Yogi stopped by, and we got a picture of him with the kids. My oldest granddaughter, Elizabeth sang at a karaoke event in the park.

I traveled with Sherri to Illinois often and remained working full-time. I had used personal and vacation time to travel with her. I even used sick time. In January of 2004, I had knee surgery, and that same day I flew (my first flight ever) to Illinois with her. We usually took the train but she wanted to get there faster. So we booked a trip on a small plane from Bishop Airport to Chicago. The puddle jumper rocked and bounced in a bad storm while lightning flashed outside the window. Sherri clung to me with fright, but she couldn't stop laughing about my first flight experience.

Once we arrived at the hospital, we discovered that her tumors had increased in her brain, and she needed extensive radiation. It required her to return to Illinois in February and stay for three weeks. I went with her but I couldn't stay because I had complications with my knee. A friend stayed with her for two weeks and our mother stayed the third. The hospital provided a lovely lodging. Sherri had her room with unique amenities for patients. Caregivers stayed in places that resembled a beautiful motel room. All who resided there could gather in a community space to enjoy each other's company. Sherri's twentieth wedding anniversary fell on a Saturday while she was there. She celebrated it with Paul and their sons, who joined her for the weekend. They had a party in the community room. The boys hung out with their grandmother so that the couple had some alone time. It was a good time for the boys. They had missed their mother.

Sherri's next appointment came up in June, and she had no one to go with her. I saw other women in her condition travel alone, and it broke my heart. I never wanted that for her, so I quit my job to travel with her. It was good that I went with her because we received the worst news yet. The radiation didn't work, and Cancer Treatments of America had run out of options for her. Sherri cried on the train ride home. She asked me to tell Paul and our mother. It would be too hard for her because she worried about the pain it would cause them. It hurt me to see her suffer. My heart broke in a million pieces for her. I would tell them for her. I would do anything I could. I never felt so helpless.

July came, and God gave me a gift, another granddaughter, Lynzi Marie. Born on a Tuesday evening, I was able to be there and see her come into this world. She had long, dark hair like her sisters had at birth. My daughter and son-in-law found the name Lynzi in a baby name book. It meant 'African tree.' Lynzi was a derivative of Lindsey. When I researched the name Lindsey, it said a place of linden trees. The Greenspire Lindens in Grand Rapids came to mind. I felt an unexplainable peace. This little one would be an excellent addition to our family, a light in a dark, sad time. The journal of horticulture, forestry, and biotechnology stated that the linden tree was sacred, a symbol of love, prosperity, fidelity, friendship, peace, justice, and altruism. It was a healing, protective tree.

I liked that Lynzi's name resembled mine. It had been six long years without a baby in the family. Sherri loved her. It touched my heart to see my sister's beautiful smile as she cuddled my new precious grandchild in her arms. My heart filled with gratitude for life.

Sherri continued to search for other treatments. She refused to give up hope. Her friends prepared a spaghetti dinner with an auction for her and raised nine thousand dollars. I continued to travel with her. Our time together filled us with joy and sorrow. My sister became my best friend. She said, "We share the same soul." I understood more than ever what it meant to be "in Christ" with another person. Nothing could ever separate us.

In 2005, Sherri went into hospice the day after Christmas. She passed gently and peacefully on the third of January, 2006. I dreamt of her after she departed. I saw her in a crowd and lost sight of her. Then, she moved through the people toward me. She didn't say a word to me but gave me the sweetest hug. When I woke, I knew that she was alive and that I would see her again. I hoped that we would meet among the sacred Linden trees.

In the bible, the Linden is called the Teil tree. *He will be like a tree firmly planted by streams of water, which yields its fruit in its season and its leaf does not wither; And in whatever he does, he prospers.* Psalm 1:3

"Being a member of Shiawassee Area Writers has improved my writing tremendously and the feedback you get is honest. I have enjoyed being around fellow writers who are like a family to me. I am so thankful to find such a great group to help me become a successful writer." ~ Jason Bullard

Jason Bullard is a graduate from Long Ridge Writers Group. He has written a short story called *The Long Walk* in the *Storyteller* magazine (January 2015) issue. His debut book of short stories is called *Strange Tales Book One.* He enjoys writing every day and reads as much as possible. His passion for creative writing started at an early age. He likes to write fiction that deals with thriller, mystery, and horror. Jason has been a member of Shiawassee Area Writers for over a year and this is his third story. He has a website at bullard.xyz. Connect with him at his email jasonbullard41@gmail.com. Jason lives in Michigan.

Jason Bullard
Happy Reading

FIRELIGHT

The summer of 89 changed Clark White's life forever. His family had planned a trip to Pyramid Point, Michigan, for some time, but it was a trip that Clark didn't want to take in the first place. But here they were, on a dirt path heading to the campsite.

From the backseat of his parent's RV, Clark watched the trees sway in the wind. For some reason it gave him the creeps, watching the tree branches appearing like claws ready to grab him.

There were many different types of RVs and tents already at the campground once they arrived. A gust of wind rustled Clark's hair as he stepped out of the RV. For the entire drive, his parents kept telling him it would be fun, but Clark wasn't convinced. He hoped that there might be some kids his own age.

Clark's dad picked out the perfect spot. A picnic table sat under a tree, near the lake. The whole scene looked like a picture out of the catalogs that dad kept in his den. Clark walked toward the lake and stood next to his dad. A boat was pulling a person in an inner tube. A smile came across Clark's face.

"You like the lake?" asked his dad.

"Yeah; can we rent a boat?" Clark replied.

His dad laughed, "Help me unload the RV and we'll check on the boats later."

Clark followed his dad back to the RV to take out chairs, coolers, and umbrellas. Mom got into the cooler and began to make everyone a sandwich. Due to the heat of the day, they decided to eat at the picnic table in the shade.

Clark finally spoke, "I'm gonna explore the campsite."

"Make sure you're careful," replied his mom.

Clark raised a hand up, walking away. At fourteen, they still treated him like a baby. There were times he wanted to yell at them. The only thing that helped him cope and calm down was to concentrate on deep breaths. As he looked around, a girl was helping her mom set up their tents. Finding the courage, he decided to go up to her.

"Hi, my name is Clark."

Looking him over, she smiled and said, "Hello, I'm Lucy."

"I take it your family dragged you up here?" asked Clark.

"No, we come here every year," said Lucy.

"Oh, I see." Clark's face turned red.

"If you want, Clark, I am going boating soon. Would you like to come along?"

Clark's face lit up with excitement, "Yes, I'd like to go!"

"Great! Meet me back here in about twenty minutes."

With a spring in his step, Clark walked back. His parents were on the shore, holding hands. It was nice to see them relaxed and peaceful.

Clark cleared his throat, "Hi, Mom and Dad."

"What's up, Clark?" asked his dad.

"I got invited to go boating."

"That's great, honey. Who invited you?" asked Mrs. White.

"A girl I just met. Her name's Lucy."

"You be careful; and check in when you get done. Do you understand?" asked Mrs. White.

"Yes, Mom."

Hurrying away from his parents, Clark ran into the RV and threw on his swim trunks. At the last second, he remembered his life jacket. His parents yelled at him, to make sure he kept it on. He nodded his head several times. The life jacket wouldn't be going on until they were on the boat. Dressed in only a bright-blue swimsuit, Lucy was waiting under a tree. She already had her life jacket on. He gave her a wave and ran up to her.

"You're going to wear that, right?" asked Lucy, pointing at the life jacket.

"Yes; I was waiting until we got to the boat."

Clark felt embarrassed not having it on. He started to put it on as they walked down a trail. The trail was narrow and only allowed a single file. She took the lead and walked at a fast pace. He had to jog to keep up.

"Do you know where you're going?" asked Clark, between breaths.

"Yes, silly; this trail leads to the dock. My uncle should already be there with the boat."

He nodded and continued to follow her. It seemed quiet to him, but then some voices could be heard in the distance closer to the end of the trail. They got on the beach and walked toward a small dock. The lake shimmered from the sun as clear water slowly lapped the sand on the shore. Clark couldn't wait to put his feet in the water; it looked so cool and refreshing.

"Hey, are you daydreaming?" asked Lucy.

"Sorry, I was hypnotized by the lake."

"Hurry up. We're almost there."

Picking up the pace, Clark walked next to Lucy. Reaching the dock he saw the white boa with a blue stripe down the side. A tall man, with dark hair, standing on it. Clark felt scared at the sight of the man.

Lucy laughed and said, "Why do you look so petrified?"

"I'm not, I'm shocked about the boat. It is so big," remarked Clark, eyeing the uncle.

Clark hated to lie, but he didn't want to look like a wimp. They both got on the boat and her uncle started it up. The boat made a low, humming sound. They backed away from the dock and took off at a fast speed. Clark enjoyed the cool breeze that ran through his hair. The sun felt good on his face.

Lucy threw an inner tube in the water and immediately jumped on. Clark watched her the whole time waiting for his turn. She bounced, up and down, over the water. After about twenty minutes, Clark got to take his ride. The water splashed all over his face. His screams echoed across the lake. He liked the speed of the boat.

"It is time we head back," said Lucy's uncle.

"Really darn...this is fun. Are you guys going again tomorrow?" asked Clark.

Lucy hesitated, "Yeah we are. I hope you can make it."

"I'll be here."

Once docked, they tied up the boat. Clark turned to say something to Lucy, but she was already gone. There was no one on the dock. He started to panic. He ran to the end of the dock, looking down the beach. The whole area was clear, except for the sand blowing in the wind.

Clark left everything at the dock, ran down the beach and looked for the trail. He looked up and down the tree line. There were tears in the corners of his eyes. The sun was about gone, casting a few rays over him. Clark didn't want anything to do with being in the woods at night.

He finally found the trail that led back to his campsite. The woods were dark. His pace was steady, but with limited visibility, he kept tripping and falling over roots.

The tears started to flow down his face. His toes hurt from tripping over the roots. He looked down and realized that his feet were bare. Clark had forgotten his shoes on the boat. Blood oozed from his toes and the pain caused him to limp.

The trail seemed to go on with no end. The woods got darker, which made it hard for him to see. The branches scratched at his face, causing him to cry out. He stopped walking. Clark knew it was hopeless to keep trying in the dark.

Clark started to say to himself, "Fire light, fire bright," a phrase his father taught him when he got scared.

Repeating this phrase over and over somehow helped him to feel better. He made his way towards a glimmer of light in the distance. A surge of hope went through him.

In a clearing, Clark saw a huge fire. People must be close. A smile came across his face. Just as Clark was about to speak, he saw a man dancing near the fire. His entire body was covered in bright red makeup. The man's face had thick white makeup.

The man looked at him, and Clark saw it was Lucy's uncle. Clark let out a scream, piercing the air. He didn't wait to see what would happen next. Clark ran away as fast as his hurt foot would take him.

The tree branches punished him as he ran through them. His breathing was heavy and rapid. It sounded like someone was following him, but he wasn't sure. All the noise echoed in his ears. Clark got through the branches and made it back to the camp. He saw his dad walking away from him, under a lamp post. He screamed to his father at the top of his lungs. His Dad turned around, waving at his son, as Clark ran to him.

"What's the matter?" His father asked.

"I got lost, then I saw Lucy's uncle dancing around a fire. He was wearing makeup all over."

"That's a shame. We were supposed to show you tomorrow night. I guess our surprise is spoiled."

Clark stepped back and looked at his dad. In a quivering voice, he asked, "What do you mean?"

"Son, we belong to a special group, we call 'family.' This year is your initiation."

Clark couldn't believe what he was hearing. Other people, from camp, began to surround him. They were chanting, "You're one of us, you're one of us." His screams couldn't be heard, over the crowd, as they closed in on him.

Clark sat up from the back seat, screaming at the top of his lungs. Regaining his composure, He looked around and realized he was still traveling down the highway in his parent's RV. They hadn't even made it to the campsite yet. A big relief came over him; it had all been a dream. His parents looked at him like he was crazy, but he didn't say a word.

"My favorite thing about SAW is the variety of genres written by our members. Our eclectic group is a fun and informative meeting of creativity and talent."

~ Nancy Thompson Walther

Nancy Thompson Walther is a poet, photographer, and blogger. Her inspiration and creativity are thoughtfully quirky and based on a foundation of prayer and faith. She has a collection of poems published in *Spring in the Mitten.*

Nancy has a Bachelor's degree in Psychology from Wayne State University and a Bachelor's degree in Graphic Design from Henry Ford Community College. Her hobbies include thrift store shopping, crafting and upcycling, gardening, going on walks, and playing Words with Friends.

Nancy's blog https://won-pet-status.com showcases her various hobbies. You can follow her Instagram: *@wonpetstatus* and on Pinterest at won-pet-status.com on her board, *Personal Pins.*

Heat Stroke

Introduction

On a hot summer day, fueled by depression and stress, my character Hope becomes ill. In part two of my poem, Hope dreams that she is in Hell. She goes through different layers of torment and suffering. If any of my readers struggle with gore, they can skip part two of Hope's nightmare about Hell, and start again in part three.

After her nightmare, Hope chooses to change her thinking. She decides to believe in God. A second dream about Heaven brings Hope visions of breathtaking beauty. She then has an epiphany that changes her life.

Hope will still struggle with stress and anxiety, but now she is armed with her namesake, "Hope." Faithfully having hope in God changes her attitude. She experiences more joy and peace in her life.

Other dimensions are conceivable, but we cannot perceive them in our three-dimensional world. As a Christian, I do believe in Heavenly realms and Hell. However, my goal for this poem is to entertain my readers with my art and creativity.

Where's Hope?

Summer blazes a wicked torch that

Feasts on Hope's air conditioner

Sanity breaks into feverish blisters

Fatigue blazes into a pendulum

Migraine rhythms drum torment
Flickering lights are halos of nausea
Reeking of forgotten fish
Spoiling on August's table

Shady voices are bitter pills
Draining away time
Raining pressure
Thundering chaos
Onto grass that needs mowing
Children screaming boredom
Dirty car windows and
Weedy flowerbeds

Hope's friends parade on Facebook
Like a bunch of clowns whose
Balloons carry rumors for air and
Floating on spikes of gossip
Fit bodies fly onto screens
Vultures looking tight jean cute
Hope's husband hovers over their candy
Licking up the sugar and fruit

Gray hair and wrinkles
Lock Hope in chains of
Expensive products with
Fraudulent keys

Bills are piles of dark clouds
Anxiety booms
Depression drizzles
Inadequacy reigns with tears
Piling junk on her cabinet of lies

Drowning Flames: A Nightmare

Devil Bunny sits on his throne of deceit
A figurine masked by sweet teardrop eyes
Long floppy curved ears, a
Blue bow snakes around its neck
Beckons her close
Offers her a rose as a gift between
Paws clasped childlike in prayer

Screams of cuteness in
Rolls of snowy fur disguise fangs with
Bloody nightmares and ears morph into
Horns that stir fear in her stomach

The blue bow grows claws violently
Grabbing Hope's neck
Nailing her throat with relentless force
Onto the blackest star

Hope explodes like a rollercoaster

Slamming her fast to Hell
Cute is darkness constricting her throat
Shooting her with missiles of agony

Devil bunny's pink flower ripens into a
Pitchfork that grazes Hope's causing
G O O S E B U M P S
Creating chills that scorch
Blackening her skin with
Shivers of Hellish heat

Foul clown-eyes
Merciless prisms
Bottomless black holes
Annihilate Hope's nostrils
Floppy ears shoot fiery darts
Pinning her charred body
Forever in darkness
Boats of puss carry her
Through tunnels of bloody rivers

Pickaxes swing tales of
Moans perfumed with stale ice
Anxiety smashes Hope on jagged rocks
Inferno's gauntlet is her noose and
A rope she never escapes

An eternity of famine tells time
By crunching Hope's stomach
Firmly in a vice like a
Vampire feeding on paradise

Hope slams down bloody waterfalls
Flowing from Satan's eyes
Piercing her pupils
Spooning out her brains
Forking them back to her
Seasoned with fire and
Boiling in her sweat

Green vapors steep Hope in moldy humidity
Roaring in her nose like a steam train
Misery whistles permanently

Vultures circle
Beaks pick
Devouring her
Over and over

Worms crawl over her
Fractured body
Eating up her decay leaving
Straw and manure

Bright ribbons of brutality scream
Swirls of color that circle back
Slaying her with layers of
Smog thick with
Expired milk and rotten eggs
Curdled with regret
Scrambled with sorrow

Saw-toothed mountains
Blaze with torches
Built from severed arms and legs
Fueled with bloody wax

Hornets fly from cannons
Stinging her eyes
Clogging her throat
Eating her bowels
Boiling them in scarlet buckets that
Bite her with sulfur
Mixed with waves of tar

Hope heaves diarrhea that
Grabs her hair
Driving her through wheels of hunger
Racing through her nose with
Aromas of raw sewage
Mixed with burnt tires

Screaming ghosts
Sew up her spine leaving
Strings of meat on her bones as
Scraps for rats and dogs

Sadness brews pots of black acid
Drops that peel off layers of skin
A flea swims in her cup
Twisting lunacy into hurricanes

Good intentions disappear
Leaving scents of skunk
Snacking on her soul

Deception loves the darkness
Craving souls
Devours goodness
Starves happiness

The Change

Bickering kids tease more migraine spasms
Record heat and humidity rule the day
Cat begs for early dinner
Phew
Only a nightmare cooked from summer's scorch
She wasn't dead

The rabbit still looks cute
Staring into her eyes which
Shutter and blink because Hope's still
Dying in the summertime heat

Red skin
Rapid breathing
Racing heart
Rumbles of vomit
Concrete wall

Hope decides she's finished and
Switches her gears
Shifting into God's love where
Serenity welcomes her with
Warm gifts from above

Songs of redeeming love rumble
Writing joyous cords
Love sings to her heart
Prayers are her music

Darkness expires
Flames of joy ignite an octave
Sliding Hope through a pinhole
Dancing into notes of light

Stars gently hug Hope
Heaven's brightest sun
Sparkles a welcome
Serenity is a breeze
Cooling her forehead

Love plus belief in God
Builds cities along
Streets painted in
Hues of honeyed glory are
Served with refreshing nectar

Holiness waits by milky gates
Pearls as tall as the length from
Howell, Michigan to Florida's Key West
Heaven's capital city shines as wide as
Michigan's Byron to Albuquerque of New Mexico
Divinity is a treasurer with a golden ruler

Heaven roars a glitter surpassing bright
Love is glorious sunlight
Seasoned with heat that doesn't burn
Flat eyes stuck in earth's three dimensions
Will never see this kingly beauty shine

Brightness

Twelve jewels are heavenly capital walls
Shining with colors alive with song, hues
Singing perfect promises of glory and
Resonating with royal rhythms
Shades that write sonnets

Jasper's wall paints royalty
Trumpeting Hope's arrival with
Diamond-like breadth
Declaring unparalleled clarity
Forged with no secrets, no shame
Pure jasper is a precious jewel
Flowing through Hope's veins

Jasper shines by sweet Sapphire's tones
Sterling azure illuminates calm while
Flaming rockets sizzle with hot snowy milk
Sugared with soothing righteous comfort
Absolute in its unique purple

Sapphire's tower looms by Chalcedony
Whose cameo layers unite as one hue
Misty gray swirls brass then
Silvery white lusters wax into
Sandy powder glazed with blue

Emerald's color writes on its wall
Rainbow armies flashing greens like gold
Smoldering praises are never melting ice
Affirming relief from Hell's summer day
Tasting like love freshly sweetened with victory

Sardonyx maroon and ivory adjoins Emerald
Pure glass petals with scarlet halos mix
Perfect shades of truth and love
Smiles that smell like lilac kisses
Float on rivers of divine happiness

Flames of goodness light Sardius's jeweled wall
Trumpeting saintly crimson tones
Fleshed in Holy notes
Parades of perfection for Hope's ears
Angels wings beat music
Calling Hope to
Fly above the stars

Chrysolite blooms with an ageless fragrance
Volcanic rays light Eden's petaled paradise
Golden greens leap for joy erupting with
Maroon amber dances of perfection
Hugging her body kissing her soul

Beryl spins next with golden wheels

Scented prisms frost into daffodil-like tulips twisted with
Scarlet roses tasting of savory green grapes
Lilies of the valley lace her mouth jewels and grins
Sending Hope through eternity's fountain
Showers of arctic fires melded with goodness and strength

Topaz paints sturdy rhombic columns
Gentle grasses form a fortress around wine-yellow hibiscuses
Sunny nectar fuels her heart with peace like a
Lion with the choicest meats kissing its ivory teeth
Security brushes tones of gold on crowns of splendor

Chrysoprasus's colors ripen measureless in bounty
Serving cake sweetened with a golden frosting
Savory emerald apples in a forested army
Celebrating with salutations perfumed with
Conifers drizzled with tangy citrus
Victory is a harvest of freedom from sadness and pain
Stories of bounty forever ringing Heaven's bells

Jacinth is a hyacinth's brimstone coloring
Deep rows of fiery truth from its mouth
Lilac frosted fruits with coppery crimson
Stamp smoky indigo seals of triumph
A stately beacon shining peace for
Life lasting ever beyond midnight
Hope fears no darkness

Amethyst completes Heaven's twelfth city wall

Perfect purple is power and authority

Sealing them with divine strength

Stripes of violet-blue blush into fairy clouds

Shapes that jolt green gospel ribbons tasting of

Savory mints stuffed with honesty

Heaven's warmth

Glorified bodies with

Time warp power

Fly through Heaven

Faster than clusters of stars

Love and hope tower over cottony clouds

Furry carpets worthy for angel's toes

Fibers weave harmony, forever

Trampling evil under Heaven's feet

Heaven's downy depths give birth to a rose

Blooming perfect petals that host Blessed cherubs on fire with God's word

Burning as orange ellipticals

Orbiting around golden rings

Ushering in Heaven's season

Divine love growing with the

Brilliance of a thousand summers

Celebrating stars carol happily
Crescent moons are saxophones
Playing the night away
Gracious with splendor
Sparkling for cosmic's pleasure
Symphonies are sunflowers
Growing in farm fields shining in
Fertile diamond-like dirt, that
Never floods and
Never sees drought

Sumptuous harvests grace celestial tables
Spices play jazz with Hope's tongue
Sweets waltzes tingle her mouth
Sour fruits are ballads for puckered lips

Heaven's gates are pearls around Hope's neck
Gifts of uncountable dimensions
Mansions sitting on peaceful golden streets
Teaming treasured companions
Citizens united in childlike love
Streaming around jewels
Light years away still hugging together
Radiating colors of pure light

Ponds swimming with gems float in cosmic gardens
Connecting rainbow collars of cotton candy

Peerless colors paint unparalleled bows
Heavenly bodies are shimmering sands around
Valleys caked with ruby-topped hills

Sugarcoated mountaintops layered with
Rings of sapphire rivers frame four-leafed Jasper broaches
Gathering emerald fields dotted by diamond tiaras
Flowing around fingers of cameo cliffs where
Trillium flowers trumpet divine love
Shouting praises are fellowship
Sounding wonders of joy

Delightful feasts between millions of friends
Conversations cross universes in a dash
Utopia doesn't tell time
Jealousy can't exist in such bounty
Multitudes of miraculous multiverses
Contain new gifts and talents to explore

Love's radiant light is freedom's colors
Sweet gifts of friends
Stars deep in blessings
Strong courage
Circles of hope
Blankets always warm with forgiveness
Simple belief brings infinite peace
Scorches of pain change into the

Sun on a calm lake

Mirrors of glory from the Brilliant one

Hate stamps an unfathomable ocean

Heaven marked its depths with peace

Freedom's fish swims in the shape of a cross

Hope is love

Redemption's gift

Forever precious

Transformed, spotless

Divine love comforts with summer breezes

Happiness lays colorful eggs

Flowers are songs and praises

Blooming with kisses

Lush grasses spin lace into prayers

Mountains bow at her command

Skies paint pictures of her happy dreams

Water waves at her finger snap

Stars beam when she winks

Animals dance along prism's edges

She knows

A butterfly's thoughts

A lion's kind words

A hedgehog's sweet touch
An octopus's secret handshake
An alligator's loving kiss
A cat's fairy tales

Hope spins webs with black widows
Weaving through celestial dimensions
Playing the violin in an orchestra of crickets
Hopping with frogs over tall
Blades of noble grassy columns

Hope is a chickadee nesting in tree branches
Whistling cheerful hymns
Directing choirs of feathered friends
Soaring together in harmony into
The Milky Way's spiraled arms
Galaxies are comfortable hugs

Season of Renewal

Angel's wings clap like lightning bolts
Foretelling cosmic visions with
Rainbow promises that fill her heart
Even grander beauty waits for her when
Her days on earth are over

Time is a masterpiece rolling around her feet
Knees fall until her lips kiss the ground

Glory is praise and brilliance
Heaven's perfection douses
Earth's scorching heat
Radiant rays of love replace flames of
Hatred, pain, and fatigue

Hope's breathtaking switch
Brings hopes
Fluffy clouds dance under her fingertips
She snuggles in its snowy warmth
Her eyes are treasures filled with
Smiles and bliss

Teardrop bunny eyes gaze are
Soulful, not deviled
Long curled ears are
Friends, not horns that
Listen without scorn
Robed in white
Baptized with prayer
Circling its waist, a sash of gold
Sunflower headdress beams eternal light
A carrot scepter paves wisdom's road

The fluff in her hands is the cat purring in her lap
The scepter is a spatula in her husband's hands
The children are bathed and in their pajamas

The cool breeze on her neck is serenity
The air conditioner trumpets softening the evening

Hope is an open heart
Radiating joy
Reborn with faith
Embracing happiness
Refusing inferno's chains

Harmony inspires a new season of
Gratitude that polishes the
Hardened dust that was
Baked onto nasty old rabbits

Freeing her of rules that nobody can keep
Freedom from perfection's bondage
Free to enjoy and celebrate life

Hope is a sculpture of
Wisdom and assurance
Awakening within her brighter dimensions on earth
As a witness for goodness, faith, and light
A stewardess working for joy, peace, and love

Hope's dreams are second chances
Life is her gift
Wrapped in heavenly love

Sealed with rainbow's promise

Floating across summer's sky

"Nothing prepared me to be the President and Leader of this great bunch of people who make up the Shiawassee Area Writers. Their motivation to learn and to be published gives me inspiration. The camaraderie helps me progress and succeed to reach my own goals. They are truly a great group of people with encouragement for myself and every single person who decides to join us on the publishing journey. I don't know what I'd do without their friendships. They have given me so much more than I will ever be able to give to them. I love each one!" ~Elizabeth Wehman

Elizabeth Wehman's writing career spans over thirty years and encompasses curriculum, periodical, journalistic, and novel writing.

Her dream has always been to write novels and Elizabeth launched her first contemporary fiction, *Under the Windowsill,* in 2014. Since then, she's added four titles to her shelf. They include: *Promise at Daybreak, Just a Train Ride, Mere Reflection,* and her latest complete historical work, *The Year the Stars Fell.*

She found the historical genre to be filled with rabbit trail research as well as walks through bygone cemeteries. The pioneers, of the early nineteenth century, reflected an amazing stamina and a determined courage to venture into the unknown. *The Year the Stars Fell* is based on a forgotten village established in the Territory of Michigan in 1833. She fell in love with the Baker family and the information she discovered about them gave way to folklore and tales of the early homesteaders. Two future novels are planned that will include the continuation of the nineteenth century farming community. The series will be called, 'The Newburg Chronicles'.

In her spare time, Elizabeth loves to read and enjoys being out in nature. Her favorite places are digging in her flower garden, listening to the birds as they herald a new day, or taking a walk on the country roads surrounding her home in Michigan.

Elizabeth has been a trucker's wife for over thirty years which helps supply the needed solitude to produce extraordinary stories. She has three grown children, four grandpuppies, and two sons-in-law.

A Lesson from the County Fair

It felt unusual for Oliver to push his son's stroller through the barns at the Shiawassee County Fair. Memories of former fairs ran through his thoughts like a movie on replay. It didn't seem that long ago that he'd asked his dad a question that would change his summer as a preteen.

He'd used every bribe imaginable to convince his parents that he could be responsible and train an animal. That first summer proved only one thing—sometimes a desire turns out much different than you bargain for.

"I don't think you realize what you're getting yourself into, Ollie." His dad held out his hand for Oliver to place a tool in it.

"I do, Dad. It can't be all that hard." Oliver gave him a screwdriver.

Dad scooted a creeper under the car he was working on. "It isn't free, you know. You have to pay up front and that can be expensive."

Oliver sat down and leaned against the tire of his dad's sporty Trans Am. The last of winter dripped off the gutter of their house onto the sidewalk beside him, but the pavement surrounding the car felt warm from the afternoon sun. Tiny spikes of his mom's flowers did their best to erupt through the cold, hard ground. "I have a bit of money saved up from Christmas and birthday gifts."

"I thought you were saving that for a bike."

"If you'd let me get a steer this year, I can save for the bike later."

Dad pushed out from underneath the car. "Hand me that ratchet."

Oliver handed him the tool, as he again slid beneath the car.

"Where will you house this so-called steer?"

"House it?"

"We don't own a barn."

"Rich said I could use his barn. His dad is a 4-H leader. Lots of guys keep their animals there."

"How about the feed and such? Who'll pay for that?"

Oliver felt his hopes dissipate. *How would he ever talk Dad into this?* But he gave it his best shot. "How am I supposed to learn responsibility if you never give me something to be responsible for?"

Dad slid out again, but this time, not because he needed a tool. An eyebrow cocked in the typical Dad questioning expression. "Say again?"

Oliver began to sweat, even though the temperature wasn't much over fifty. "You know. It'll teach me to care for an animal. Be responsible. I promise, it'll be all on me. I can get some extra papers to deliver on my route."

Dad rolled his eyes. "I understand your dilemma. I really do, but son, I don't think you understand all that goes into preparing a steer to show at the county fair. It's hard work."

"And a great chick magnet, too."

His dad chuckled. "You have a specific one in mind, son?"

Oliver couldn't lie, but if he didn't change the subject, his dad would never forget the girl comment. "C'mon Dad. Give me one year. If I don't do well or it gets too expensive, I won't ask again."

"How about this?" Dad sat up on the creeper, waving a screwdriver like a pointed finger. "If you do well, you can continue. If this ends up being way too expensive, we'll never have this conversation again."

Oliver tried to not let his excited facial reaction change his dad's mind.

Dad added, "But hold on. You know Jim down the road?"

Oliver nodded.

"He told me he wanted to give two sheep to someone to raise for the fair. We talked about it Sunday at church."

"Sheep?"

"Yeah, let's start on something a little easier to handle than a twelve-hundred pound hunk of beef. What do you say?"

Disappointed, Oliver had always wanted to show a steer, but what would be the difference between a steer and a couple of sheep. Perhaps his dad was right. "Okay. Sounds like a plan. Will you call him today?"

"I'll ask the next time I see him."

Oliver didn't know much about farming. He lived in a subdivision. Yet often he'd daydream about farm life. Two of his best friends lived on farms. He loved hearing about their daily lives, often envying the thought of having farm animals and caring for them. *How hard could it be?*

Oliver's plans interrupted his schoolwork. It was all he could think about. *Should he name them? Maybe he could ride his bike to Jim's farm.* He couldn't wait.

Dad soon confirmed that Jim would allow Oliver to raise two of his new lambs to show at the Shiawassee County Fair. After supper one night, Dad drove him to Jim's farm where Oliver had the chance to meet the lambs for the first time. His sister and mom tagged along.

Jim led them out to a barn. Inside a small stall, two young lambs bleated in fear as they approached.

"These will be perfect to show. They come from good stock. Nice color, too. If you do it right, they'll win big at fair." Jim opened the gate so Oliver and his sister could get acquainted with the noisy lambs that scurried into a corner.

Oliver held out his hand. "C'mere, little guys. I won't hurt you." But the two lambs wanted nothing to do with their new caretaker. Oliver scolded his sister for her quick movements and loud voice. "Shut up, Mattie. They'll never come to me with you around."

Dad scolded Oliver for being mean to his sister. "Stand here quietly Mattie, and see if Oliver can approach them."

Jim explained that it would take time for the lambs to warm up to him. He decided to name them Curley and Moe after his dad's favorite television show.

For the first few weeks, Oliver's dad drove him to Jim's farm in the morning and at night to do chores. Oliver assured him that when it got warmer, he'd ride his bike.

Jim taught him how to properly muck out a stall. He also taught Oliver how to approach the sheep so they wouldn't be so timid. Jim taught him how to raise healthy lambs and prepare them for competition.

In early May, Oliver began riding his bike to do sheep chores. He had to get up three hours earlier to make it to the farm and back before the school bus. Night time was easier, but sometimes he missed supper. Mom usually heated up his plate after he arrived home.

He must have been doing something right because the lambs grew. Oliver loved watching them jump around their stall when they saw him coming to feed them. He felt needed.

When school let out for the summer, Jim told Oliver he'd need to spend more time with the sheep. "You need to teach them to set-up properly to show and then lead them around the barnyard so they learn to obey your commands."

It took Oliver until noon everyday to finish his exercises with the lambs. Instead of feeding them first each morning, Jim encouraged him to keep them a bit hungry so he could reward their good behavior with bits of feed. "They'll respond better if they're hungry."

Soon they began teaching the lambs to brace. Oliver used his knee to push back on their front haunches so they'd stand firm against their back legs, but for some reason Curley and Moe couldn't get the hang of it.

The next day, Jim encouraged Oliver to take his lambs out to a puddle in the driveway. "Lambs hate water. Let's show them the puddle behind them, surely they won't back up into that."

Oliver pushed back on the lamb's chests but it didn't seem to matter to Curley and Moe. They backed into the water anyway. Jim could only rub his chin at the predicament. "Never seen anything like it."

As much as they tried to get the sheep to cooperate, the lambs refused to brace against Oliver's knee nudges.

Oliver worked hard to get the sheep to obey. He led the sheep around the yard until he was sure they'd follow him. One day, he decided to take a chance at unhooking them from their leads. What happened next could have been a segment on the World's Funniest Video show. When the lambs were let loose, instead of following Oliver, they ran into the busy road. Cars had to stop as Oliver led the sheep back into the farmyard.

"You better walk them around more, Oliver. They aren't ready to be on their own yet," Jim told him.

Friends from school often called to ask Oliver to meet them at the skate park or see a movie, but Oliver had to turn down almost every invitation. As much as he wanted August to arrive, summer fun was slipping away.

Each day took longer to train the now-grown sheep, whose

stubbornness increased, too. Leading them around the yard on a hot July day, Oliver began to doubt his decision. They still weren't bracing as they should and when afraid, the pair would run to the barn at the slightest loud noise.

One day he asked one of his farming buddies about his issues with the lambs. "I never thought this would be so hard."

"I don't think people realize all it takes to get an animal ready for fair. My sister and I are not only working with our steers, but we have pigs, rabbits, and a turkey. You should be happy that all you have are a couple of sheep."

Oliver wanted to be happy about his decision, but walking and attempting to brace his sheep grew monotonous. The sheep still weren't responding to Oliver's training. On occasion they would brace, but more often than not, they would tilt their heads at Oliver, as if to say, "*We don't get it.*"

Two weeks before fair, Oliver's dad asked about his progress. "Are they ready to show?"

Oliver felt particularly discouraged that day. He'd tried hard to use every tactic Jim had taught him. The sheep still refused to brace. "I don't know what I'm gonna do. Worst of all, I can't win a trophy, let alone a ribbon if I can't get them to stand firm for the judging."

Oliver's mother spooned him an extra dollop of whipped cream on his strawberry shortcake. "That's for your efforts." She shrugged. "They might surprise you, Oliver."

"Hurry up and finish your shortcake, Oliver!" Mattie squirmed in her seat. Dad put his finger to his lips, and shook his head.

"What's wrong with her?" Oliver's patience with his sister was growing thin, too.

"Can we tell him, Dad?"

"Oh Mattie!" Dad rolled his eyes, and smiled. "We have a surprise for you after dinner, Oliver."

As soon as the dishes were done, Oliver's family led him out to a corner of the garage. There they had something square, covered with a blanket. "Daddy and I painted something for you." Mattie danced around the garage, giggling in excitement, then uncovered the surprise.

In the corner sat a wooden chest, painted black with silver stripes. Oliver's favorite colors. In bold silver print was his name and below it were Curley and Moe's.

"You can't go to the fair without a tack box for your things." Mom smiled.

Every 4-H'er had a tack box for fair. Oliver felt proud that his work was beginning to pay off and soon he'd be showing an animal at the fair just like he'd dreamed of doing for years.

Oliver opened the storage container as Mattie held up two silver harnesses. "We got you these, too."

The surprise helped Oliver get through the next two weeks and soon they were loading the sheep onto a trailer to take to the fairgrounds. Oliver had grown close to the ornery sheep under his care, however he was anxious to have the project completed.

Fair week was a whirlwind of activity for Oliver and his dad, who'd taken the week off to help him. They shaved, washed, and combed Curley and Moe to perfection for the competition. Oliver sat on his tack box, during his hours off, to watch the people admiring everyone's sheep.

The days were long, but fun, heading to the fairgrounds early each morning and back again at night to care for Curley and Moe. On Wednesday, it came time to show. Would he win a trophy, a ribbon, or nothing at all? Oliver woke that morning with a queasy stomach. He stared at his sheep, trying hard to envision them bracing and following him as he'd taught them. Yet despite all his hard work, the sheep may not cooperate in the show ring.

His dad joined him right before he went to find seats for the family. "Oliver, I'm proud of you. You've worked hard to get these sheep ready."

"But what if they don't do it, Dad? What if I look like a fool? These sheep have a mind of their own."

His dad smiled. "Kinda like us, huh? We often want our own way. We hate when people like our boss, parents, or even a teacher at school, tells us what to do. Most of the time, they're only trying to help us find our way. Even you." Dad folded his arms.

"Me?"

"You don't always want to follow through with what your mom or I ask you to do. Soon, you'll be doing life as an adult. But the best I can do is to teach you a good path. Whether you do it or not, is up to you."

"So what does that mean for my two stubborn sheep here?" Oliver held tight to the leads of the sheep. He could envision them both darting down the midway, plunging into a nearby trash barrel for any scraps of carnival food, if he didn't hold tight.

Dad patted his shoulder, "Have you done your best?"

Oliver nodded, "I think so."

"I know so. I've watched you get up early and go to bed late. You've taken on extra chores to pay for feed. You've worked hard. I'm super proud, Oliver. But son, they'll do what they know to do. It might not be what you want, but you've given them the tools they need."

Oliver stood taller. Because of his hard work, he knew what it took and had greater empathy for the kids who had given up their own summers to care for an animal.

"Son, you've already won, in my book."

It had been years since he'd been in the ring with his sheep. Oliver lifted his two-year-old son higher to point out the sheep in a nearby pen. "Look, Henry? It takes a long time and hard work to get a pair of lambs ready for fair. Trust me. Maybe someday, you can do just what your dad did so many years ago." The sheep bleated, causing his son to jump and reach for his mother.

Oliver's wife asked, "Did you win that year, Oliver?"

He stood taller and smiled. "Yes, I got best-of-show my first year. But now, I realize I got something better."

His pretty wife tilted her head at him. "What's that?"

"I learned that despite our best efforts, we don't always win. But we need to work hard and try. I hope Henry can learn the same lesson." Oliver tousled the toddler's hair. "Hard work doesn't always get a ribbon, but for me, it was a lesson I never want to forget."

"Diana was first introduced to the Shiawassee Area Writers in February 2019. A long-time family friend, Maureen Gilna, encouraged her to attend a meeting. Diana received such a warm welcome from the group. She knew, immediately, this was the place to grow as a writer. She was reacquainted with old friends, and soon made many new ones. She found the group to be very approachable, knowledgeable, and encouraging. Diana has gained confidence to face her inner critic, and to visualize herself as a writer." ~ Diana Vernier

Enjoy Diana

Diana Vernier is a fifth grade teacher at Laingsburg Elementary School. She received her Bachelor of Science Degree from the University of Michigan-Flint and her Master of Education Degree from Marygrove College in Detroit. She has a passion and enthusiasm for writing that started in high school. She encourages her students to keep a journal to express feelings, and enhance reflection of their daily life.

Vernier resides in Owosso, Michigan with her husband, Andrew. She has four adult stepchildren, and 10 grandchildren. She loves to spend time with her husband and family. Her heart is full of joy when she can spend time with her grandkids. Her summers are spent mostly outdoors in her flower gardens, having quiet time on her patio with a cup of coffee, and reading.

The Day the Music Stopped

Pain is real and it is a part of life, but getting through the mental and physical suffering is about mindset. It's about choice.

It's been years, but the pain I am feeling has revealed its ugly head once again. The old familiar lump has returned to the back of my throat, but it no longer has its grip on me.

The most pivotal thing is to give yourself the time to work through your emotions without getting stuck. That's why writing about this arduous journey is an important part of my life story.

It was August 1996, and the Shiawassee County Fair was in full swing when I saw Lance. I had no idea he was even in the area. As I approached my favorite place of the fair, the dairy barns, the smell of hay and manure filled the air. I had stopped to talk to a few friends, when I noticed him. He stood next to the FFA Dairy barn, holding a freshly squeezed lemonade from a local vendor. His younger brother was with him. When Lance's and my eyes met, we knew we had to approach each other.

After taking a big sip from his oversized drink, he gave me a hug and said, "Wow, it's been a long time, huh?"

"Yeah, it has. What, 12 years?" I replied and turned to acknowledge his brother with a hug.

After some small talk, his brother left us to walk around the fair. We caught up on what we had been doing over the past several years. As we talked, it seemed as if no time had passed at all.

We must have walked through the commercial buildings and animal barns multiple times. Being so caught up in conversation, I was oblivious to the sun sinking, but the smell of French fries and elephant ears made me realize I hadn't eaten in hours.

As we approached the Ferris wheel, the enticing flashing blue, red, and purple lights caught my attention. We ran to purchase tickets and got in line. As the wheel spun, we eventually stopped at the top. We had a stunning bird's-eye view of the county fair with all its beauty. It was a picture-perfect evening and I didn't want it to end.

For the next several weeks, Lance and I continued to see each other. We reminisced about old times in the youth group, but now we began to make new memories. One heartwarming evening while holding hands, we walked along the Shiawassee River near Curwood Castle. The sky was clear, and the stars twinkled above us. Fireflies danced in the distance. It was a too-good-to-be-true night. One I wanted to preserve forever.

We continued along the edge of the Shiawassee River heading toward the Curwood Castle Bridge listening to the evening sounds as we walked. When we arrived at the foot of the bridge, my breath caught as Lance took my hands in his. The moon was beaming off the river creating a stunning reflection of the castle in the water. The warmth of his hands, and the butterflies I felt, made my heart race. Lance, at that very moment, got down on one knee and recited, as if he had been practicing for weeks, "Diana, I am not perfect, but you have made me see that I can be a better person with you in my life. Would you marry me?"

I hesitated. I had to slow down my racing emotions to process it all. My heart said one thing, my head another. It was the most romantic thing anyone had ever said to me. I felt like I was standing there for hours fighting over a head versus heart decision. Was it too soon? I had known Lance most of my life; why was this decision so hard?

For Lance, I am sure the silence probably seemed like forever. I didn't want the moment to get away. It's a moment every woman dreams about, so why was I struggling to answer.

"Of course" I blurted out, but did I really mean it? It's every girl's aspiration, and for me it was no different. I would begin a happily ever after journey with my best friend, my soulmate. Little did I know that this "fairy tale" dream had already started to develop cracks. Neither one of us could wait to tell our parents the exciting news. Lance was so excited after I said yes, he quickly pulled his phone out of his pocket, nearly dropping it over the bridge and into the river.

I waited to tell my parents until the next day; I wanted to make sure it wasn't a dream. It turned out it wasn't, and soon we set a date to be married, August 30th, 1997. Many things needed to be done, but I had just been hired for my first teaching position. That needed my full concentration; I had plenty of time to prepare. As the year progressed, amazing things were happening. I loved my job. I was able to purchase my first house: a two- story farmhouse. The paint was peeling, the roof needed repairs, and the wallpaper needed to go, but it had good bones.

With the help of family and friends, I crossed a few preparations off my wedding "to do" list. Lance left most of the wedding plans to me. He knew how much it meant to me. This was my first wedding, and I wanted everything to be perfect. I found an elegant dress, and an ideal venue. My parents and I went to several caterers, and finally found one that fit within our budget.

I was so caught up in "my wedding world" and doing things for me that I wasn't listening to God's voice because I was afraid of what I might hear. I was filling my schedule with distractions. I had always heard, "Don't leave God out of your life, especially your marriage. Make Him the center of everything you do." Yet God has a way of getting our attention, and He soon got mine.

Lance and I had been busy with our daily schedules, so it didn't allow us to spend time together as we would have liked. It had been two weeks since we last went out together. I finally went to his parents' house to see him. As soon as we connected again, I noticed a change in him. He seemed distant and secretive. When I confronted him, he became agitated and said I did not trust him. He even looked different. His hazel eyes had lost their sparkle. They seemed more dilated and black. I didn't know what was going on; call me naive, but at that moment, I was.

I needed answers, so I decided to have conversations with some of his family members. I had known them for years. So I called Ray, Lance's older half-brother, and his wife, Cathie, and arranged to meet them at their home. As I filled them in on Lance's odd behavior, neither one of them seemed surprised.

They spoke with compassion as they shared their knowledge about his past life under the influence of drugs. I felt paralyzed. As if I'd just been kicked in the gut with a steel-toe boot. How could I have been so naive?

Was I that caught up in the "bliss" of being married that I had missed the signs? I was always told never to go back on your word; I'd made a commitment to marry Lance. But I didn't want a life that included being chained to an addict. I felt betrayed and I needed deep healing. As a band aid fixes superficial wounds, I needed a strong defender; a soul healer. I should have listened to my head and not my heart that night on the bridge. Life does change people, and you really can't say you know someone unless you spend time with them. I needed to confront Lance, and soon.

Hands sweaty and downhearted, I picked up the phone and dialed his number. His mom answered. Lance had not been home over the past few days, and she did not know where he was. I asked her to have him call me as soon as he returned. Hanging up the phone, I knew there was nothing more for me to do but wait. My heart was anxious but my soul was heavier.

Like my house when I first moved in, I was alone and empty. I was too ashamed to talk to my parents and family; what would they think or say? I was in so much emotional pain that I didn't know where to start. I have never cried so hard that it drained my soul before. I felt without purpose: void of life. I realized that I had been overwhelmed instead of seeking peace, happiness, and God's kind of joy. I needed healing, but I was too busy surviving.

The small voice that kept coming back to me. "Don't leave me out of your life. I'm here for you Diana, please talk to me."

I knew God was trying to get my attention, but I felt unworthy. I also didn't want to ignore His words, so I embraced them, and took them to heart. I felt so empty inside, and my body was physically weak. There was nothing left to hold me up. It was at that moment I heard God's voice tell me not to panic, but to be in His presence. Relish His peace. I needed to stop worrying and let God take over and heal my heart which only He can do. In the arms of my Lord, I could feel the healing begin.

Lance finally returned home after about a week. He had been on what is called a drug binge. His choice of drug: cocaine. I confronted him, and this time God had given me the confidence and strength to do so.

Of course, he denied his drug use, and chose lame excuses as to why he had been gone for so long. He had become a masterful con artist. After months of the same thing, I could see his life spiraling out of control and he desperately needed help, not only physically, but spiritually, too.

God has designed us with a purpose in mind, and Lance was no different. I believed in second chances, and I wanted to be there for him. I gave Lance an ultimatum. I told him he would definitely lose me if he didn't check himself into a rehabilitation facility.

The next day, with the help of his family, Lance was admitted and ready to spend the next three months in South Carolina at a faith-based drug rehab facility.

Lance graduated from rehab in the month of December. South Carolina was beautiful and warm. His mom and I were both so proud of him. He was asked to give a speech on how the program helped and how it encouraged him to want and hope for a healthier future.

On the car ride back, Lance told us about the last few months and the changes he had gone through. I really could see a difference in him. He appeared to have changed for good and his will was strong, but would the knowledge and resources he received from Faith Home be stronger than his desire for drugs? I guessed time would tell, but at that moment, I was delighted he was coming home.

For the next eight months, Lance remained drug-free. It was an enjoyable time. I was so relieved and thankful. We spent a lot of time talking about our future. He joined a local AA meeting, and I joined a local Al-Anon group to become more educated, and gain an understanding about the world of addiction. I wanted to support and encourage him emotionally through the days, weeks, and years ahead.

As the days turned into weeks and weeks to months, it really seemed that Lance had been able to kick the drugs. We decided to go forward with the wedding plans for August 30, 1997.

So, once again I started making preparations for the big day. I had my dress altered, called the florist to make a few changes, and finalized the caterer. In a few days, the invitations would be going out; it was now just weeks away. I could almost hear the pianist play "Canon in D".

Even though the wedding was approaching fast, I continued to hear that small voice. But this time it was saying, "Don't just hear with your ears, Diana, but most importantly understand with your heart."

One week before our wedding, and with everything prepared I couldn't foresee any problems, except for one. I couldn't visualize myself walking down the aisle. Maybe it was cold feet, or maybe it was God trying to keep me from making a big mistake or protecting me from tremendous pain. I knew I needed to discuss these feelings with Lance and see if he felt the same way, or if it was just me. I prayed for quite a while before I left. I asked God to give me peace, strength, and a clear mind as I talked with Lance.

It was late when I arrived. There was a light on, so I went into his house. The same sensation I experienced before he went into rehab closed in on me. I began to breathe heavily and I could feel the pounding of my heart. I didn't see Lance, but the pain in his parents' expression said it all.

I asked if they knew his whereabouts. Both answered they hadn't seen him all day. My wounded heart hit the floor, and I fell onto their couch mentally exhausted. The music had stopped. I just knew he had relapsed.

I didn't understand until much later that an addict needs to come to the end of him or herself to make a personal decision to want to get better. Lance went to rehab for me and not for him. What do I do now? The wedding was on Saturday, five days from now. I had guests and family arriving from out-of-town, so I waited.

The next two days seemed like years as I waited for Lance to return. I even drove around looking for him, and hoped I wouldn't find him dead in an alley. After a few hours, I gave up and returned home to wait for my sisters to arrive. There is no quick fix for a broken heart; it takes time, but most of all it needs Jesus and His unconditional love. I prayed for healing, forgiveness for Lance, and wisdom.

It is only by God's goodness I felt his presence and the love of others as He spoke to their hearts when mine was so afflicted with pain. The void in my heart had its own journey ahead. Left deeply bruised, it wouldn't be easy. But, my heart and soul longed to feel joy deeply, be thankful, and listen for a new song. My dear sisters, Joan and Penny called all the guests and even waited for over an hour at the church just in case they had missed anyone.

My loving family, with their empathetic hearts, helped me through the emotional week as I canceled all the wedding plans. It was an embarrassing time in my life, as I had to swallow my pride. I was crushed to think of the money and the time my family had put towards making that day special. My parents, however, were very supportive, but I wasn't sure how I was ever going to make it up to them.

But God is good. It was a miracle how He worked through people, and spoke to their hearts when I was plagued with much devastation. It was a true miracle that all our money was returned except the deposit on the caterer. As for the cake, my family and I gathered together the Saturday I was to be married, and enjoyed our own family celebration.

"I have loved you with an everlasting love, with unfailing love I have drawn you to myself." Jeremiah 31:3

Valued by the Creator

Hold tight when the storm winds blow,
and don't allow the turbulent seas of life
carry you off course and cause you to
lose hope.

There will be days the rain and winds strike you hard
and seem to never let up, but know, this too, is temporary.
Some storms linger while others may
come and go.

We have a Savior, an anchor, a shelter. His name
is Jesus. He may not always calm the storms, but
He has promised to calm you through them.

God never promised life would be easy, but rest assured He
strengthens, refreshes, and transforms. Look for the
blessings that come from it. Hope rises above the pain.

Though our hearts may still be tender, hurting, and bruised. We can
rejoice in His truth, breath in His name, and feel our burdens lifted.
Re-centering ourselves in Him because our hope is firmly anchored
on the cross.

We are valued by the Creator. Be filled with great joy.
He gave His life that we might live. To Him be totally

submitted. So stop trying to hold yourself up, and
sit at the feet of Jesus.

"The name of the Lord is a strong tower, the righteous run to it
and are safe"
Proverbs 18:10 NKJV

"The Shiawassee Area Writers is a wonderful group that provides encouragement and the extra push to keep going. They have helped me focus on my writing and made me realize what my true passions are in all of my artistic endeavors. They have put me on the path with my aspirations of working as an editor and have opened up my world for publishing stories and poems." ~Tracey Bannister

Tracey Bannister is a First Class Petty Officer in the U.S. Navy and works as a Mass Communication Specialist. She has published works online and in newsprint from military assignments in the Baltic Sea, Pearl Harbor and Japan. She graduated with a Bachelor's degree in Journalism and Mass Communication at Ashford University and also received a Bachelor's degree in Business Administration from Central Michigan University.

Tracey is featured in SAW's previous anthologies, Winter in the Mitten and Spring in the Mitten. She is a native of Midland and currently resides in Owosso. You can read more works from this author at http://dreamcatcher.pressfolios.com/

Enjoy the poems!

Tracey Bannister

Captain Ray

~dedicated to my grandfather, Aaron Ray Havens, 1925-2000,
Navy Veteran~

On those sunny Sunday mornings
the rays sparkled on the lake
And we all grew with excitement
on the journey we would take.

Gas, check; oil pressure, check;
gages work, let's go!
Oh wait, don't leave yet!
can't forget the radio!

We piled on the boat
and picked our favorite seat,
Then clicked on that stereo
to hear the Polka beat.

Captain Ray was at the helm
puffing on his pipe,
In his blue jeans and Captain's cap
he looked the stereotype.

We cruised up and down the shore
gazing at the view

"Oh wow, look at that house,
that one is brand new!"

Under the bridge and into canals
we drifted along at Grandpa's pace
"It's an easy Sunday morning,
it's not a gosh darn race!"

Oh how I miss those Sunday mornings
the boat rides on the bay
And oh how I miss
our dear sweet Captain Ray.

Midsummer's Race

~dedicated to Arthur Duane Hignite (Thor), 1938-2006, Army National Guard Veteran – "Let's go racing!"~

Summer's here and I can't wait
It's finally Friday night
I get to watch the cars spin round
Underneath the bright track lights

The engines roar and the dust flies
As they make their practice runs
This isn't just a hobby
Racing gets into your blood

Which one do you think will win?
My dad always asks of me
My friend and I both yell in unison
"Anybody but Eddy"

That black car looked a menace
Painted just like #3
But Earnhardt he was not
And I prayed he wouldn't lead

Round and round they went

This race was the best
For that black car on the track
Put every car to the test

The only car that could beat him
Was inching up the backside
Here we go, it's getting good
He's in the turn, now let it slide

There's only a few laps left
Can the blue car get it done?
Will this finally be the race
That Eddy gets outrun?

They're neck and neck down the stretch
Oh they run so close
Everyone is standing now
The finish should be grandiose

One wrong move is all it takes
When the cars run this way
And sure enough, a little bump
And the blue car starts to sway

The final flag has fallen
And the cars screech to a stop
They both had hit the wall

When the checkered flag was dropped

We all stood in disbelief
No one knew who'd won
The announcers said, "stand by"
As they checked the final run

But spotters know, eyes in the sky,
Who reached that moment first
That pile of a wreck had won
The blue car of Senneker's

Never had I seen
Such an awesome sight
Both cars were hauled away
To the garage that night

And the blue car was victorious
He left Eddy in the dust
My hero was the winner
Now let that black car rust.

Rise from Death Valley

As I lay here in this hospital bed
wondering what's going on
It all comes flooding back to me
the things that I'd done wrong

I remembered that I woke up
just a few short days before
And found a note that simply said
"I can't do this anymore"

My job, it wasn't easy
weekends and long days
A deputy's work is never done
and he didn't want to stay

When I went to work, my day got worse
my boss said it didn't matter
For if I left, he could replace me
I was a walking disaster

I packed my stuff and scooted out
I didn't say goodbye
I knew no one would miss me
so I didn't even try

I stopped off at the liquor store
bought some whiskey and some rum
Drove way back in the woods and thought
how could I be so dumb?

My thoughts returned to last year
I needed to get away
I came out west and naively thought
things were gonna change

But problems, they hang with you
even though scenery might change
Your troubles won't go away
just 'cuz you're out here on the range

So I put the pistol to my head
and then I pulled the trigger
But the bullet jammed inside
that shiny metal cylinder

Now what am I going to do, I thought
as I looked across the pond
My plans hadn't gone any farther
than that stump I rested on

I sat there in the summer sun

the heat was bearing down
Can things get any worse? I asked
as I threw my thoughts around

I got back in my pickup truck
and headed down the road
The only place that I had left
was the place that I called home

I scrambled up the front steps
and opened up the door
But something hit me hard
I was knocked down to the floor

A man ran through the hallway
as I reached down for my gun
But it wasn't there and so I had
to just get up and run

The man's face, it was familiar
a dirty cop I'd ratted out
He was seeking his revenge
with his gun, he left no doubt

The bullet struck my shoulder
my body crumpled to the ground
Is this the way it's gonna end;

will my listless soul be found?

Then you were there, by my side
saying "please don't go,
I need you more than ever
my devotion, you'll never know"

You weren't sure how to tell me
what you really meant to say
Back there in the office
on that truly awful day

You had no way of knowing
that my marriage was dissolved
You wanted to say "please stay"
but felt I had issues to resolve

That fateful shot changed everything
when you came to my rescue
You gently whispered "stay with me"
I can't do this without you

Now I look up from this hospital bed
and see your smiling face
And I'm not sure why I ever
wanted to leave this place.

Angela Clayton

"Since becoming a member of the Shiawassee Area Writers, I've been able to meet other published writers who have helped me learn about writing. I'm learning more about the craft. How to bring my art to life and shape my words into pictures to share with others. I have met many talented authors since being in this wonderful group." ~Angela Clayton

Angela Clayton has enjoyed reading books from many genres throughout her life, passing her love of reading down to her now grown children. She has dabbled in writing off and on since high school, but it wasn't until she was introduced to Shiawassee Area Writers that she began to learn more about the craft to bring her art to life and to shape her words into pictures to share with others. She's met many talented authors through this wonderful group. When she's not writing you can usually spot her along back roads or swampy areas taking pictures of wildflowers or insects. Once in a while her family obliges her by letting her use them as models. She would like to thank her husband, Matt, for his patience and great sense of humor during her learning process.

Lakeside Camping

"Amelia, what *did* you do?"

"It's okay, Sara. It'll all make sense soon. Look at page four. These lines meet," I grunted as I stretched, "the top loop up there. Then we connect it."

Looking unconvinced Sara replied, "Sure thing." My friend Sara and I needed this getaway to Lake Michigan to catch up and reconnect. I had a notion we were going to have a great weekend, just the two of us.

While we put the last touches on our campsite we heard singing and raucous laughter from somewhere close by. We gave into our curiosity to see where it came from. There sat two guys a couple of campsites across and over from ours.

I glanced over at Sara, who appeared excited at our new discovery. I pulled at her shoulder, "Let's get our fire started so we can have dinner."

Sara, face alight, exclaimed, "Wow! Did you see those guys? They're cute! Didn't you think so? Especially the blond?" *Here we go. When Sara got excited about something she talked fast.* "They were singing. They could be rock stars."

I almost snorted. "Yep, saw them. Heard them, too." *I seriously doubted their rock star status.* How could I distract her and get her back to our site? "You hungry? I'm hungry. Let's figure this fire out."

I should have paid attention during Dad's fire lessons, soon our fire turned into a disaster. There was smoke everywhere, but hardly a flame was seen. Sara began to cough and ran around the fire.

"Amelia," Sara said as she fanned her hands to clear the air, "I think something's wrong." I was already down on my hands and knees on the ground, sorting it out.

"Hey! Need a hand?" A deep, male voice called out. I could hear him but I couldn't see him.

Sara spoke up in a helpless tone, "Yes! It just went haywire."

A soft voice sounded close to my shoulder, "Do you need help?" Since I couldn't see squat I assumed I wouldn't be the one to get it going anytime soon.

As I stood, dusting the dirt off, Sara continued, "You're the guys from the nearby campsite, right? We heard you singing earlier."

Sara and the blond began to talk while the guy with the darker hair looked like he was doing something to the fire, but I couldn't see what exactly.

Suddenly a horrifying feeling erupted in my chest. *For real? We were "rescued" by those yodelers? Can this day get any worse?*

I cleared my throat, "Sara, where's the water? I'd like to get cleaned up."

Sara's voice dropped. "Well, there's a shower down the way."

"We have no water at all?" I hated to ask for this clarification.

"Just what we brought to drink."

Why did she sound peppy when my eyes were stinging, watering, and I still couldn't see? I could feel my cheeks burn and I just wanted to vanish.

When I returned from the shower, our fire was roaring. "You're back. You look so much better." Sara was roasting dogs and drinking water. "How do you feel?"

"Better." I replied. "Those look good." My stomach began growling.

"They're almost done. Here, have a drink." Sara handed me a bottle of water.

We passed the rest of the evening over s'mores, getting caught up on life in general, and then I fell asleep with Sara going on and on about Jasper and Rob and their heroics with the fire.

Jasper? What kind of name is Jasper?

As Sara and I settled into our chairs on the beach the next day, a light breeze took the edge off the bright sun. Our perfect day was soon interrupted by some boisterous talk not too far away. Thankfully, my dark sunglasses allowed me to people watch without being too obvious. *Oh Lord! It was the two beastly, yet helpful, guys from yesterday.* Maybe Sara wouldn't see them or their noise would blend in with other beach hullabaloo.

No such luck.

Sara gasped and her big smile returned. "Hey! I think I see those two cute guys from yesterday. You never got to thank them for helping with our fire." She looked at me like a disapproving mother. "Maybe you should thank them."

"Oh, I guess that does sort of look like them," I feigned

uncertainty. "I'm sure you thanked them enough for both of us." I leaned back in my chair, opened my book, all set to relax.

Before long a shadow fell over me. "Hello there! How's it going?" One of the guys had made his way over to us and was blocking my sun with his big head and blond hair. His friend with the dark hair was right behind him, digging his toes in the sand and his hands into his pockets. I decided since Sara wanted this interaction she could have it and I'd hide behind my book. She obliged.

"Hi guys." Sara began, as she tried her hand at flirtation, even though her face turned crimson when she spoke. "We're great!"

The blond one answered her in return, "Well, Jasper and I had hoped to bump into you."

Sara actually yanked on my arm. "Did you hear that, Amelia?" Nudging me, "They hoped to bump into us," Sara whispered.

I decided to play dumb, as I rolled my eyes behind my sunglasses. "Hmm? What? This is a *great* book." Looking up I tried to sound disinterested, "Oh, hello." I squinted as if in thought, "Who are you?" I asked the guy *still* blocking my sun. I thought I heard a faint chuckle from behind him.

The guy, who turned out to be Rob, smiled and said, "We rescued you yesterday."

Rescued? I didn't need to be rescued.

Jasper jumped in, "Ah, I think he means we helped you. But you probably don't recognize us. How are your eyes? Besides beautiful."

Well, isn't this great. Guys never compliment me on my eyes, and the one time someone does, I'm trying not to notice how cute he is.

"My eyes are fine, thank you." Standing to my full five feet, four inches, I suggested, "Sara, let's let these gentlemen enjoy their beach time and we can grab some lunch."

Sara smiled and said, "Later!" as she waved over her shoulder.

Later that night when we got back to our tent we found two bouquets of wildflowers propped against the tent door flap. My bouquet had a note: *Want to hang out tomorrow? We'll bring coffee at 8am. Sleep well, Jasper.*

So, is he, like, a stalker or just a nice guy who happens to want to spend the day with me while presenting holy nectar? It's a good thing I took that self-defense course.

After we talked it over, Sara and I agreed that if the guys offered to bring coffee they couldn't be all that bad. I was glad the four of us had agreed to start the day early at the beach. We lingered in the water, hung out on the beach, and enjoyed general shenanigans. Sara and I built a sandcastle in between breaks of sunning ourselves. Jasper and Rob threw a football back and forth.

We walked along the shoreline. At one point, Sara and Rob

strolled off hand in hand, leaving me and Jasper all alone. I hadn't even realized I'd stopped walking, I was too caught up in looking at the never ending blues and greens of Lake Michigan, and feeling the soft sand under my feet. The waves had me hypnotized until I felt an arm slip around my waist. I was surprised but tried hard to play it cool, even though it tickled.

Jasper's smile was shy and lopsided, "I wasn't sure I'd enjoy this weekend alone with Rob. Then, I saw you and those pretty blue eyes." Jasper held both of my hands. "You're easy to talk to and it's been fun getting to know you. I guess I'm trying to say, I like you."

I'd never been in this situation before. My palms were sweaty, I hoped Jasper hadn't noticed. I just started to speak, "I like you too." *Smooth. Tell him how you really feel.*

Jasper smiled as he pulled me in for my first kiss at twenty-three. It had to have been the most perfect one. I declared it so.

As we walked back, Jasper held my hand. We found our friends just as the sun began to sink beyond the lake. Rob and Sara were already there with burgers and fries from a local stand. With all of the playing and the walking I realized how hungry I was. The food smelled heavenly.

As dinner wrapped up we noticed the sky began to light up. We watched as the fireworks danced in the sky for us. I was stunned from both the sight and the fact that the guy holding my hand really liked me. As the bangs and pops got louder I jumped and was soon enveloped in his arms. I decided this would be the best Fourth of July of my life.

The Bear

Summertime camping with small children is always fun and interesting, especially when you bring your dog along. Our's was an aging beagle/basset mix named Chloe. She was mild tempered, but was usually quick to alert us to intruders. A favorite memory from around the early 2000s was when we took our young children, Bethany and Noah, and our dog Chloe on a trip to the Northern Lower Peninsula. We found a nice spot, nestled in a forested area.

I made sure Chloe was secure so she could wander around and sniff things out. The kids played tag, with Noah occasionally stopping to look at the bugs he was fascinated with at that time. As soon as he became distracted Bethany hid from him, then his incessant hunt for her went on while my husband Matt and I went about setting up the campsite. Man, was she great at hiding.

Trying to wrangle our very young and quite curious son Noah away from a blazing campfire was an adventure itself. Roasting marshmallows to turn into crunchy, gooey s'mores was fun. The kids left scattered pieces of skins from burnt marshmallows they had thrown at each other all around the campsite. I picked them up the best I could, to make sure we didn't attract ants, or other pests.

After walking Chloe, I was able to get the two kids settled and tucked in. Then Matt and I began the task of trying to get comfortable on the air mattress. We finally settled in for as good a night sleep as we could manage.

From dreaming I was on a storm-tossed boat, to being awoken

by Matt shaking my shoulder, calling my name, "Angie. Angie. Wake up." He tugged on my arm while whispering in my ear, "I think there's something outside."

Trying to get my eyes to cooperate and open, I asked him, "Did you look?"

"No. I waited for you."

I was so sleepy. "What's going on?"

He whispered a little harsher, "I *said* I think there is something outside of the tent."

Okay, something. Not someone. A thing is better than a person. A thing can be dealt with.

"So look outside and see what it is." I pointed toward the tent's zipper opening.

Unzipping the flap he looked outside. When he ducked his head back in, his eyes were wide.

He whispered, "I think it's a bear."

I couldn't believe it. I gasped, "A bear?"

Matt sighed in exasperation, "There are black bears around here."

Not being from Michigan, I wasn't sure what to believe. I had been fooled into believing far-fetched stories before. To think that I was camping in woods inhabited by bears caught me off guard.

"Where's the food?" I asked. I was certain we had put it back in the van, but I had to ask.

I could hear the tone change in his whisper as Matt answered, "I think it got left on the table while you were getting the kids down. I was playing with the dog."

If there was a bear out there we couldn't just sit in our tent and whisper about it. "Well go out and chase it off then Matt."

I pictured my big, strong husband emerging from the tent, flashlight in one hand, a branch ready to be used as a weapon in the other. I imagined him chasing off the cute, yet dangerous black bear.

What did he do? He grabbed my sneaker and flung it out of the tent flap!

I was in shock. I hissed at him, "My shoe? You threw my shoe?" For emphasis I slugged him with my pillow, but took it back for fear he'd throw that out too. He actually laughed about the situation.

"I didn't know what else to do," he said while still laughing.

I was not laughing. "Did you at least hit it?"

"I'm not sure. Hey," Matt said suddenly. "Why don't we let Chloe out?"

Matt checked the connection to her stake, then she was out of the tent, baying like she was on the trail to save our lives. Matt was right behind her with his flashlight, while I was left to hop behind, looking for my other shoe.

We followed Chloe's baying to a large tree. Once we showed up, she quieted and sat there, her nose pointed up. Matt's flashlight beam followed her gaze where we found our "bear".

There sat a large raccoon. He clung sideways high up in the tree, contemplating every possible way of escape. Finally, that little pest took a giant leap. Somehow he was able to soar over our heads. Chloe made an immediate about face, she raced as hard as she could, stretching her tie-out to its limit, until she could see him no more. She sat down, then looked back at us, as if to ask if she had done her job. We were still standing there, stunned at the stunt the little fellow pulled. Matt assured her she did a great job at scaring off the bear when he squatted down next to her, petting the top of her head.

Then Matt and I looked over the table with his flashlight. The only thing that suffered any damage were the marshmallows. I hoped the raccoon enjoyed his sticky late-night treat while trying to give us heart attacks.

The three of us decided to head back to bed. It was only when we got back to the tent did I realize that the kids had slept through it all. They've heard the story multiple times over the years. It's one of their favorites as well. After that night Miss Chloe exuded a self-satisfied air about her until her final nap. She was a wonderful, beautiful dog.

"As our writing group grew in numbers, we shared many of our writing talents with each other. These group members have been my cheerleaders. Having the group affording my works with gentle critiques and ideas, has given me trust in my writings and given me support and confidence to pursue my goals. Knowing that we are all in the same boat as writers, we help each other achieve our dreams as successful authors." ~Maureen Gilna

Maureen Bishop Gilna has been a member of the Shiawassee Area Writers since 2017. She has been active in her church and community and has resided in the Owosso and Corunna area all her life. She graduated from Owosso High School in 1956,
Maureen pursued and received a Bachelor of Science Degree when she was 54 years of age. She has received many community awards of achievement throughout the years and continues to serve her community. She has been involved in the Memorial Hospice Program in Owosso, Michigan since the early 1980's.

Through the years, Maureen has written poems and articles for various farm magazines and local newspapers. Her book "Be Not Afraid in the Presence of His Light" was published in 2013. In that book, she shares the spiritual and miraculous moments of her near death experience.

Maureen lives with her husband, Richard, on the family Centennial Farm in Corunna Michigan. They are the parents of 5 children and six grandchildren.

On Hallowed Ground

During my high school years, I made many lifetime friends. These friendships were memorable and lasted well into my adult life. Sally was a spunky, fun- loving friend who, with a twinkle in her eye and a smile on her face, could hold her own ground in any spicy debate.

Approaching middle age, I was working at a local home hospice agency as a staff employee. The hospice office received a call from a member of Sally's family. They requested assistance for Sally's care as she had just been diagnosed with a terminal illness. The family had been caring for her at her house. They expressed the desire for her to remain there and receive hospice care through her final days. Sally was received into our hospice program. I volunteered to be on the care team.

One very warm Fourth of July morning, I was asked to make a visit to help Sally and her family as her death appeared to be imminent. I was greeted at the door by Sally's husband Ted. After tears and hugs, he escorted me to Sally's room. As I approached her bedside and took her hand in mine, she opened her eyes and gave me a slight grin. I informed Sally and her family I would be at her bedside for as long as I was needed. I suggested to the family that they take a rest and time out for nourishment.

Sally was very emotional. It was difficult for her to rest and accept her condition. She confided that she knew she was dying but was not ready to go quite yet. The medication was relieving the pain and she began to grow sleepy. I took her hand in mine. Whenever I made a move, she opened her eyes to be sure I wasn't leaving her bedside. My voice seemed to calm her as I assured her I was not leaving her.

There was one moment she opened her eyes and in a weak voice uttered the word "soap". I instantly remembered an incident in our high school years, when we both got in trouble for soaping our friend's windows on Halloween. I laughed a little as she smiled. Her smile left her as she began to cry. She turned her head away from me. I asked her if she was afraid of dying. She confided that she knew she was dying and she was not afraid, but just wanted to stay a little while longer. I knew Sally believed in heaven as we both attended the same church when we were younger. I asked her if she still believed in heaven. "Of course I do!" she answered emphatically, "That is where I am going!"

I continued the questions. "Is there someone that you would like to take your hand on the other side?" There was silence as she fought to stay awake. Then with a weak voice she whispered "Jesus." I informed her that I would continue to hold her hand and when Jesus took her hand she could let go of mine and take His.

The hours grew long. I had been sitting bedside for six hours. Sally had entered a very deep sleep. The hospice nurse had been in the house for several hours and planned on staying as Sally's death neared. The family had rested and was seated in the living room. They came to Sally's bedside periodically to give Sally a kiss and gentle words of love. I could hear the family in the living room visiting and recalling their good times with Sally. Laughter was followed by tears as they shared these memories. Ted had visited his wife many times. He spoke of his love for her and reassured her he would be all right.

The cool summer air softly drifted into the room through the open door and windows of the house. My bedside vigil was into the eighth hour. The crickets were just beginning their serenade. Suddenly, I felt Sally's hand moving as she weakly squeezed my hand. Her eyes briefly opened. I put my face close to hers as she whispered, "Pray for me." She then let go of my hand.

She was still breathing slightly, but I sensed that her spirit had left at that point. I turned toward the living room and summoned the family to return to her bedside. I remarked to them, as they formed a circle around the bed, how privileged it was to be with one who is dying. I reminded them that we are standing on hallowed ground as the Lord approaches to take her home. I then asked them to pray per Sally's request. When the prayers had ended, the nurse took Sally's vital signs and announced that Sally had stopped breathing.

To provide privacy for the family, the nurse and I had left Sally's room. This was a time for family to say their good-byes.

I stepped outside onto the porch. The night seemed especially dark. Wiping the tears from my face, I gazed at the sky. On the horizon I saw a burst of lights and heard the snapping, cracking, loud booms of the town's fourth of July celebration. I smiled to myself. I knew Sally was walking with her precious Jesus and the celebration I was now witnessing, was just for her.

Best Date Ever

Arriving, as scheduled, in the late afternoon of a warm sun filled summer afternoon, he looked so handsome. I was hoping he would think the same of me. I was about to have a date with this wonderful man! How exciting!

I had spent most of the day preparing for this special date. My nails were manicured and polished to perfection. My hair was curled and styled to the best of my abilities. I had spent much time selecting just the right dress and accessories for the occasion.

Leaving my home, we left the driveway and proceeded to an out-of-town destination. My date selected a very fine restaurant where we would enjoy a wonderful meal together. We began in conversation immediately. We had so much in our lives to catch up on. He listened to my thoughts and comments as I brought up memories of our lives throughout the past years. Before we realized it, we had arrived at our destination. As we entered the restaurant, we were approached by a friendly staff. As we were seated, I looked around the room and was impressed by the beautiful and warm décor. It made me feel comfortable and happy to be there.

Ordering our meal, we indulged in a special drink that was a favorite for both of us. We again began sharing our life memories. Some were humorous and wonderful, and others were serious. I looked at his eyes as we were sharing and I was filled with so much love for him.

The food was delicious and very enjoyable. We ate so much we had no room for dessert. He suggested that we leave and he would escort me to a very famous ice cream parlor on the nearby campus where he attended college. What a great idea! Ice cream was my favorite dessert.

We left the restaurant and proceeded to our destination. It took us a short time to arrive. Upon arrival we found the place closed for the day. How disappointed we were. Then my clever date had an idea suggesting we enjoy our ice cream at a popular ice cream parlor where he and his friends frequented when he was attending college.

As we began our journey to this ice cream parlor, he expressed his interest in touring the campus of which he attended to obtain his degree. One structure after another housed the academics required for his degree; Chemistry, Research, Botanical, and various other scientific facilities. I also shared with him my activities in some of the same buildings.

As we left this campus, I realized his love for his career. It warmed my heart and made me love him so dearly. Following this special tour, we ambled towards the ice cream parlor which was located just outside of the campus. Many students and their friends were already enjoying their ice cream treats as we approached. Waiting in line for only a few minutes, we purchased our favorite flavor of the frozen dessert. We looked for a place outside to sit and view the oncoming sunset. Finding a bench, we sat down to enjoy a conversation as we ate our ice cream.

Beautiful golden and orange rays of the sunset were visible for all to enjoy. All too soon, darkness of the night began to take over. We decided to leave this special place and return home.

Our journey home seemed to end all too soon. We never ran out of conversation and topics to talk about. What a wonderful date! What an everlasting memory to treasure always.

Arriving home, it was time to say goodnight to the love of my life. We walked hand in hand from the car to the front door of my home. Few words were exchanged. I did not want this evening to end. It was time to say good night. I reached up and gave him a big hug and a kiss on the check. "Thank you so much for a beautiful and memorable day. I love you so dearly, Grandson, and I will always treasure this special time with you."

"I have been a member of the Shiawassee Area Writers for over two years. Although we write in different genres, we are cohesive in the support of each other's work. We recognize the challenges of writing along with the passions necessary to meet those challenges, and we are there to assist each other with those challenges." ~ Sally Labadie

During forty years of owning and operating the Love Funeral Home with her husband, ***Sally Labadie*** saw how the village of Bancroft was losing its rich history with the death of the once active community leaders. This inspired her to compile *The History of Bancroft; A Pictorial History of the Town and Its People,* and to direct the Bancroft Historical Society.

Her own personal history of teaching and administration in the Corunna Public Schools was published in *The Good, the Oops! And the Funny, Events in the Life of a Teacher*, and was followed by *And You Thought I Retired,* memoirs of post retirement work in the Department of Education at Michigan State University. She continues to write memoirs of her life in rural Bancroft, Michigan, where she lives with her husband, Harold.

Teaching children has always been her mission, so she published seven picture books and one chapter book; *Wooster the Rooster, Tanner's Turtle, The Schoolhouse Mouse, What's Under All Those Leaves, If I Had a Dinosaur, The Story of Honk, the Goose, Little Puddie Cat, and Mystery on the Cliffs.*

She is also a prolific writer of memoirs of her life in rural Bancroft and of adventures while fossil hunting with the Friends of the University of Michigan Museum of Paleontology. She is a volunteer at the Historical Village in Corunna, at Elsa Meyer Elementary School in Corunna, and is a trustee with the Corunna Educational Foundation.

The Case of the Flying Dog

Summer, 1997

There are times we of the Zolkosky Clan must say, "It could happen only to Mother!" As a member of the family, I can say this is one of those times.

One must first picture the street in front of her house, five lanes, the main drag between Ypsilanti and Ann Arbor, and the main entrance to Eastern Michigan University. Years ago when a center-turn lane was added, the grassy space between the sidewalks and curb disappeared. As a result, the narrow sidewalk abuts the curb.

Last week Mother was walking Duncan, (her Scottish terrier), and was almost back to her driveway, when she was thrown to the ground by an unknown force. As she lay stunned, a man got out his car and came to her. "Are you all right?" he asked.

"I think so," she said, in a confused manner.

"I don't see the dog," he added, after which he quickly got in his car and drove off.

A second car stopped, and a couple got out. The lady ran to Mother's neighbor's house to call an ambulance, and the man stayed with Mother. He told her what he had seen. A black lab was running across the street, and the other car couldn't stop. The car hit the dog, throwing him into the air and into Mother. The dog wasn't hurt, and he ran off. He was nowhere to be seen. The driver had left the scene as well. The neighbors, alerted by the lady, came out and put Duncan in mother's yard. He was still on the leash, and the leash was still clutched in her hand.

Mother refused the ambulance, and had the neighbor call my sister, Wendy, who drove her to the hospital. They found a small cut on her head, a skinned arm, and possible bruised ribs. When she had chest pains a few days later, she went to her doctor and had x-rays taken. The pain was caused by a cracked rib and she was given pain medication.

She remained in pain all week, but was able to laugh at being hit by a flying dog, and I'm sure Wendy got a kick out of relaying the story to family members and friends. The *Ypsilanti Press* even ran a story about it the next day, titled "Lady Hit by Flying Dog," so there was no hiding the story from the community. After all, how many of us hear of a "flying dog," let alone getting hit by one?

Wild Woman

1994-1995

I never realized what a wild woman I was until I spent three weeks in Alpena with other avid fossil hounds. In the summer of 1994 I stayed in my small trailer at a local campground. Paleontologist Bob Carr was tenting, and our friend Bob House had his pop-up camper for a week to be our chief cook. His wife and son were to arrive a few days later.

When you are camping for an extended period of time, regular chores must be accomplished in addition to fossil hunting in quarries. Washing clothes is one of those chores. After a few days working in the hot, dusty quarry, Bob House and I decided to go downtown to wash clothes. The laundromat was very clean and an attendant was on duty. Bob and I went in together, washed our own clothes, sat together and talked, dried the clothes, sorted and folded them and left together. The attendant, of course, watched us as she did everyone.

About five days later, Bob Carr and I went to do laundry. As it would happen, the same attendant was working. We went through the normal routine, but with strange looks from the attendant. As we sat talking and waiting, I wondered why we were receiving those looks. Then it dawned on me. Here I was, a gray-haired, middle aged woman coming in twice within a couple weeks, with different men to do laundry. What a wild woman!

On the final week of our stay I went by myself to wash clothes. Since I was alone, the attendant felt free to talk to me. She laughed when she found out what I was doing there with more than one man.

But there's more!

The following year I returned to help Bob Carr find fish fossils for his research. Another teacher, Bill Hummel, joined in the fun. On the day before I was to leave, we headed for a point that extends into Lake Huron which is a favorite fossil hunting spot. The lake bed is made of slabs of limestone that holds fossils (If you are lucky enough to find one). We wore rubber shoes and waded into the lake. The algae was thick and slimy. We worked around the point, having no luck. Bob, along with his blond Labrador, Dusty, went near a cliff to check out a retaining wall.

Not being the most graceful thing, I worked carefully by myself near the shore, carrying a bucket and a hammer, and Bill waded farther out in the lake. Suddenly, I found myself falling forward into the water. I held onto the bucket, and probably that did the most damage. I stood up, and the pinky on my left hand stuck out almost at a right angle from my hand.

There was no pain, and since I am not a person to panic, I calmly called to Bob and said, "I think I'll need to see a doctor." Bob meandered back, in his usual unworried manner.

"It's probably just dislocated," he said.

"No, I think it's broken." (And he teaches anatomy, I mused.)

We stopped our hunt and waded through the reeds back to where the trucks were parked. For some reason, when I go near water, I always take extra clothes. The guys let me change, and then we drove to the hospital in town.

It was a hot afternoon, and we didn't want to leave Dusty (Bob's dog) in the truck, so Bob headed back to camp and Bill and I went into the emergency room. It wasn't long that an x-ray was taken. The nurse decided I needed to see a doctor, so a local "hand" specialist was called and asked to come in to look at the finger. Within an hour he was there. I had really smashed the finger, and surgery would be needed to insert pins.

I had to change into a lovely white cotton gown, and was told to give my purse to my "husband."

"He's not my husband," I responded. Well, try to explain that you are camping together but NOT together. I briefly explained it, but what difference did it make? Bill waited out the surgery. When I came out, still in my lovely white gown, a different girl said she'd get my "husband."

Then she said, "There's another man who keeps calling to check on you and wanted to know when you'd be leaving the hospital." Oh, boy. Here's that wild woman again. Bill and I laughed when we told her what was going on.

After almost three hours we headed back to camp. I had three pins sticking out of my finger, covered by a large bandage. I needed to keep my hand upright and I decided I couldn't drive the big dodge truck pulling the trailer on the four hour drive home. I called my son, Ed, and he and a friend drove up. Ed drove the truck and me home.

Two weeks later, I started my new job as a principal with my hand still bandaged. When the children found out I was injured while FOSSIL hunting, they thought I was a heroine.

Briars and Brambles

July, 2008

"Well, they ran through the briars and they ran through the brambles,

They ran through the bushes where the rabbits wouldn't go.

They ran so fast that the hounds couldn't catch them

Down the Mississippi to the Gulf of Mexico."

Those are some of the words to Jimmy Driftwood's song sung by Johnny Horton, "The Battle of New Orleans. And those were the words that I sang heartily as I headed out of the woods on a six-wheel Polaris, after picking wild blackberries.

My son, Ed, had told me about the ripening blackberries, and thought maybe I could get enough to make some jam. It was a nice morning, so after I had the laundry started I went to the farm and hopped onto the six-wheeled beast. I drove down the dirt road, unlocked the cable that keeps unwanted guests from entering, and went down the lane to the back of the field where Ed had said some berries were growing. I found a few, which I picked. Looking around I spotted some nice rocks in the edge of the field, which I thought were perfect for landscaping around our soon to be new house, which we named Southpark. I loaded them in the dump trailer of the Polaris, and slowly drove along the back of the field, through the woods and behind the next field of soybeans. I found a handful of berries before I came to a rock pile, where I loaded up a couple more large rocks, all the time walking through poison ivy. Did I know that the nasty plant was there? Yes, but I had on jeans, and wasn't worried.

I went back to picking a few more berries when Ed came through on his tractor. He was going toward a back area of the woods to cut down a couple dead ash trees that were possible "widow makers" in the next storm. I showed him what I had, and he asked if they were enough to do anything with. "Well, maybe for a couple bowls of cereal," I answered.

After he left, I turned to leave, but decided to go back and take a second look. I found I had missed some huge bushes. Oh, oh! I had to make my way through more poison ivy and brambles. My arms were scratched and my hands purple from the berry juice. That's when I thought of the son, and that's when I started singing it with gusto. I picked my way back out of the woods, and then headed down the road to the end, where I knew more bushes were growing. And actually, I didn't care if anyone heard me singing. It was just a spontaneous reaction to the event.

I parked the Polaris in the entrance to a neighbor's field, and walked back to the bushes. Talk about briars! I was inside a mass of berry bushes, and yep, poison ivy, but I found many more juicy morsels. It looked like a deer had been lying there, but who one would lay in the prickly briars is beyond my understanding. I filled the container and then walked down the side of the field on a last ditch effort to find more.

I found a few more ripe berries, and then headed to Southpark where I unloaded the stones so they would ready when I had the area prepped for them.

In all, I found a little more than a quart of berries, so upon returning home I put them in the freezer to keep until I could gather more in a few days and then make that yummy jam.

I stepped out of my old tennis shoes, socks and jeans, (while trying to avoid touching any oils from the poison ivy,) and put them in a basket ready to wash. I went upstairs and washed my legs and arms in case I had oil on them. My arms were scratched, but to me that wasn't a problem.

I thought back to when my father used to take us into the woods to pick blackberries and raspberries, and sometimes gooseberries. We never found enough to make jam with, but enjoyed them in our cereal. However, I don't remember them being in poison ivy or brambles. I also love picking strawberries and blueberries, but those are in cultivated fields, and the only problem might be a few mosquitoes.

And now the new words to that old song:

"I searched though the briars and I searched through the brambles,
And I searched through the bushes where the rabbits wouldn't go.
I picked so fast that the critters couldn't find me,
Down the wooded lanes and the brushy fence row."

"SAW membership has meant a lot to me and has helped me grow as a writer. I value other member's feedback and opinions about my writing, as well as the camaraderie that our small group share."
~ Gracelyn Keys

Wishing you health & wellness!
Gracelyn Keys

Pamela McKee writes under the pen name of ***Gracelyn Keys***. She is a children's author and a mental wellness advocate. She is working on writing and illustrating several picture books on various mental health topics to help children understand more about these challenges. She is a member of the Shiawassee Area Writers Group and Society of Children's Book Writers and Illustrators. Her books are titled, *Knock, Knock, Who's There, Bear? A Story About Embracing Bipolar Disorder.* Follow GracelynKeysAuthor on Facebook for future releases.

She has a bachelor's degree from the University of Michigan in clinical community psychology and a master's degree in business administration from Central Michigan University. She worked in the human services area for over twenty-five years. She resides in Byron, Michigan, with her husband, Dachshund dog and thirteen chickens. She has three married children and eleven grandchildren. She and her husband love the outdoors and vacationing on the Straits of Mackinac.

Summer on the Straits of Mackinac

Summertime means relaxing fun-filled trips to our quaint and cozy cottage on the Straits of Mackinac with my husband, Bob, and black Dachshund dog, Bruiser. We call the dog, "Bru" for short. Trips up north often include visits from our large extended family and two other dogs, another Dachshund and a big Boxer-Pit breed. We purchased the cottage on Lake Huron overlooking Mackinac Island about nine years ago. We spend each summer working on it, while also enjoying memorable things to do in the area with our family.

Summer on the Straits is filled with fantastic fireworks, dark star-studded skies, and chilling around the roaring fire in our hand laid, stone, fire pit, with a refreshing drink in hand. Mackinaw City hosts a magnificent firework display and laser show each Friday night in the summer. On Saturday nights, nearby St. Ignace hosts a parade of spiffed-up cars or trucks on their main drag, followed by an equally awesome firework display.

While sitting near our beach on the Fourth of July, fireworks can be seen from Mackinac Island, Hessel and Cheboygan, while Mackinaw City and St. Ignace simultaneously provide their own grand display. On these nights, fireworks light up the sky on the Straits. Grandkids wearing glow bracelets play in the yard on the tire swing or in the hammock. They carry sparklers carefully in their hands as they write their names in the air with sparks. Lazy dogs lounge by the fire or simply follow the grandkids around hoping for dropped food.

A spectacular panoramic view of the northern gleaming skies can be seen at the *International Dark Sky Park* located west of Mackinaw City, along Lake Michigan. Clear summer evenings require an early start, long before dusk, to obtain a prized parking spot within the park. Otherwise, there will be a long walk through a spooky, forest lined road from the overflow parking area to the lakeside. Moon craters, shooting stars, and many well known constellations can be viewed through toy telescopes and binoculars. Phone flashlights help illuminate the dark pathway. While very rustic a few years ago, today, the park boasts a new observatory and well lit, paved parking area. A lakeside hike at dusk reveals a breathtaking and unforgettable sunset over Lake Michigan.

What summer would be complete without a trip to Mackinac Island? Bob and I stay on our compact power boat in the marina for a few nights each summer. We used to be avid boaters before we bought the cottage. Nowadays, boating trips on the Straits and fishing excursions are infrequent, but nonetheless treasured. We usually boat to Mackinac Island in the evening when most tourists have already departed. Once the boat is secured to the floating dock, we take Bru for a leisurely stroll down the main boardwalk in town. He is often afraid of the horses and the crowds of people who want to pet the cute little weiner dog, so he shies away from outstretched hands until he feels more comfortable with the atmosphere. At dusk, the cannon at *Fort Mackinac* fires, a bugler can be heard playing "Taps" from a distance, and this is our cue to exhaustedly head back to the boat to sleep for the evening.

In the morning, we ride our bikes around the entire eight-mile long island. We explore famous sites along the way, like *Arch Rock* and the *Grand Hotel*, and stop to skip a few stones across the lake's surface. We visit our favorite eateries; buy fudge and pizza, which makes for delicious snacks back on the boat. We play bocce ball on the lawn in front of the fort and people (and horse) watch. We have brought the kids and some of the grandkids for day trips here, but many times, it's just the two of us and Bru.

Every time we visit, we find new things to explore. One time, we found a cave deep in the woods and a ravine, called the *Crack in the Island*. It can only be seen walking along a long, narrow, forest trail in the middle of the island. It was well worth every step of the hike. One of our other favorite island finds is the *Butterfly House*. What a marvel to have a delicate butterfly land on your shoulder or on a child's finger. We love all the special wonders of the island!

Back in Mackinaw City, we enjoy biking on the North Central rails-to-trails pathway. This trail is located across the street from the cottage. We have a huge collection of various sized bikes for our family and friends to ride when they visit. The younger grandkids enjoy trying out the co-pilot bike or the child carrier, both of which hook behind an adult bike. We love to bike ride into town with them, which is about three miles away. We reward ourselves with ice cream, a walk around the town shopping center, and allow the kids to play in the park. We will often cruise down to the *Mackinac Bridge Park*, where many families gather near or in the water.

On the ride back to the cottage we look for berries along the path, like wild strawberries and blueberries, depending on the time of year. We search for birds, chipmunks, and wildflowers near the wetlands. On hot days, large black snakes coil up in the sun along the side of the trail near a swampy area. They slither back into the marsh when we draw near. All of these discoveries provide much animated chatter for the ride back.

Every trip includes at least one hike down the path to *Mill Creek Discovery Park*, which is a short distance from the cottage. We often take Bru for a walk there in the evenings. The flowing spring fed water can be heard long before it can be seen from the path, and a fresh dewy scent abounds when we get close. The grandkids like to play on the bulky, concrete, forest animals in the park and also on the mini zip-line. Small trout can also be fished for in the creek near the Mill. There are many hiking paths inside the park to explore, as well. We have seen various wildlife, from deer to coyotes on our walks, but have yet to meet a bear (although we have seen bear tracks before). There is also a long zip-line, a tall climbing wall, and a swinging rope-bridge for the older grandkids and adults to enjoy (at an extra cost).

Playing on the beach and in the water back at the cottage is always fun for everyone. We have a big green plastic container full of beach toys and dump trucks for the kids to enjoy (and adults too). Creating fanciful castles surrounded by water-filled moats is always a must while on the beach. Passing ships and sail boat regattas are mesmerizing to watch on the Great Lakes. Jumping over the waves along the beach is fun or taking a refreshing swim to cool off from the summer heat. Me, I like to rake the beach. I have found some unusual things that have washed up, like a child's shoe or a ship's thick, twisted, nautical rope. It's my own way of playing in the sand. I find it relaxing and satisfying when the beach is raked clean again.

Our other water toys include a canoe, two one-person kayaks and a family-sized paddle boat. We enjoy using the boats in the morning or later in the evening when the lake is serene and free from white-cap waves. The water is crystal clear and tiny fish or other swimming animals can easily be seen from one of the small boats. One time, we saw huge carp circling the paddle boat while trying to paddle over to a sandy spot called, *Charlie's Point*, near the *Mill Creek Campground.* The swarming fish scared some of the kids, so we quickly started back to our beach area.

When the grandkids come for a visit to the cottage, we plan an annual treasure hunt in the yard. It's especially fun if all ten of them (another is only a baby) are there for the hunt at one time. They run from sticky note clues to the next clue until they find their dollar store prizes at the end of the hunt. Last summer, tiny hand-sized rocks were painted red, along with one inspirational word painted in white, and hid around the yard. Once found, the kids traded them for prizes such as candy, bandanas, stickers, and glow bracelets to use around the campfire. Although the treasure hunts only last a few minutes, the kids look forward to them when they visit each year.

My husband, Bob, enjoys spending time on the porch swing in the backyard overlooking the water, and I enjoy gardening and getting my hands dirty. The cold frames used in planting our favorite vegetables in early spring bloom all summer with fresh herbs, radishes, lettuces, Swiss chard and onions. These cold frames are mini-greenhouses built below ground and work better than a larger greenhouse in this northern area. We grow cherry tomatoes too, but have had no luck growing green peppers that far north. Wildflowers bloom all along the front of the cottage, as they are freshly planted each spring season to enjoy in the summer. They provide an array of beautiful colors next to the Lake Huron rock border stacked around the cottage. Large blooming hydrangeas are a must in the Mackinaw City area, and grow well near the lake. I also grow beautiful mums, black-eyed Susans, daisies, hostas, daylilies, and wild roses. Every summer, I try to plant at least one new perennial in the yard to determine if it will survive the harsh winter weather and grow again the subsequent summer. The calm beauty and familiar scents and tastes at the cottage never fail to renew my spirit.

Many outstanding summertime memories have already been made on our trips to the cottage, too many to write about. Whether it's listening to the gentle lapping of the waves, as we sit near the crackling fire and talk about our day and our dreams for the future, or watching fireworks in the star-studded sky lakeside, it's always a northern Michigan treat. Boating, biking, hiking, swimming, and exploring many of the tourist destinations in this northern Michigan area keep us actively engaged with nature along with our large extended family. Even the treasure hunting is memorable for all. Our summers are packed full of adventures at the cottage; however, we also look forward to a little down time in the peaceful, colorful, quiet of autumn when summer has ended.

"When I joined SAW, more than two years ago, it gave me opportunity to mingle with and learn from folks who share my passion for creative writing...to tell stories, some true—some not.

Our meetings are fun-filled, with informal lectures, apropos games, occasional parties, and enjoyable comradeship with authors young and old, experienced and not. It's kind of thrilling to see one's imagination in print."

~John Morovitz

John Morovitz

John Morovitz is an eighty-six year old retired physician who refers to himself as a "recreational writer." Much of his literary dabbling has been satirical, sometimes nonsensical poetry and essays for friends' special events. On occasion, he has composed poignant eulogies and commemorative verse. As an author with minimal formal training, he "writes as he reads," non-critically; for entertainment or to learn something.

John's only significant work is a self-published mini-biography of a much beloved industrialist and philanthropist, Mr. George Hoddy. Pending for some time has been a family memoir that focuses on the Christian love that overcame the rampant post-war hatred of the Japanese.

Big Al and the Five Footer That Got Away

A fish story

I've never been much of a fisherman, and I'm still not. For an impatient cuss like me, angling is about as exciting as standing in line for a flu shot. I reckon that attitude stems from a couple dismal childhood experiences, sweltering on the hard wooden seats of a becalmed row boat, with nary a nibble; watching others reel them in. Though I'm not particularly squeamish, I never got much pleasure impaling helpless minnows and crawlers on barbed hooks. Even more distasteful was helping others scale and disembowel their catch; especially since I never really relished the taste of the slimy critters.

Things changed, however, when I married Joanne, in 1958. With that sacred compact, "'til death do us part," I also acquired a father-in-law, Albert Raymond Preston. While most of his family called him Bert, to friends and colleagues he was Al, or "Big Al." It didn't take me long to feel comfortable calling him dad. Of course, there were times when my brother-in-law, Ron, and I would blurt out, "Where the hell's the *old man*?" when he had snuck off for a nap, leaving us to finish the work. We might have added a few expletives when he'd return ready to start another project, and we'd be ready to drop. In fairness I must say he was a good worker well into his ninth decade.

I'm pretty sure my father-in-law was pleased and maybe even proud to welcome a young doctor into his family, especially one who would eventually present him with four precious granddaughters. I sometimes wondered, though, if he wasn't a little disappointed I wasn't as much of an outdoorsman as himself.

"Big Al" was raised on a very poor dirt farm, lacking in-door plumbing, telephones, and with only minimal electrical service. Horses were used for plowing. Such humble existence, however, instilled much self-reliance and ingenuity. Even as a youngster, I'm sure he had honed skills and talents I could only envy.

Complimenting his many innate skills, dad's degree in electrical engineering equipped him to do almost anything he attempted. He was a competent carpenter, mason, plumber, and electrician; skills he used to build three homes. He taught auto mechanics, repaired small engines, and taught himself to play the electronic organ he had built. He dabbled in photography, coin collecting, baking, and some sewing arts. His was an impressive resume', to say the least.

High on Albert's list of pleasures were camping, hunting, and you guessed it, *fishing.* His three daughters had pretty much passed through those stages, and I'm sure he envisioned a son-in-law sitting in the bow of his home-made dinghy.

At one of our early Christmas celebrations he presented me with my first ever shiny, metallic green Shakespeare rod and reel, and a tackle box full of little gadgets I couldn't even name. It could mean only one thing.....I was going to be a fisherman whether I wanted to or not.

The following summer provided the earliest opportunity to visit Albert and Alma at Cedar Lake. The latter spans most of the nine miles between Oscoda and Greenbush, a couple resort towns on the "sunrise side" of the big mitten. It was a challenge to pack all the necessities for a family of five into the trunk of our Chevy Biscayne, before carefully placing my new fishing gear on top. I must say I was quite proud how I had completed that task so efficiently. With everybody on board I slammed the trunk lid down and we eagerly started on our way for a long week-end on the water.

A three hour ride with three restless young'uns was always a test of patience, but Jo and I survived. We were greeted by two anxious grandparents who quickly whisked away the kids, leaving us to unpack the car.

To this day I remember my dismay at the sight of four inches of my still virgin Shakespeare protruding from, and crushed by the trunk's lid. It was a moment of frustration and unimaginable embarrassment. My first thought, "How was I going to own up to my incompetence, with 'Mr. Perfect'?"

Did I mention Big Al was a prototypical Type B critter? He uttered no snide aspersions, only a little conciliatory humor and, "It could have happened to anyone." Within the hour he had the rod functional and looking almost normal.

Cedar, in years past, had been known as a fisherman's lake, and like so many others bore rumors or myths of the "Big One" lurking in its depths. Not exactly a "Lock Nessie", I would have surmised it to be an oversized pike or maybe a lost muskie. Personally, I had my doubts, since all I had ever seen coming out of that water were what most folks deridingly refer to as "Cedar Lake perch." A dozen or fifteen might satisfy too, if they weren't too hungry, and there are plenty of fried spuds.

It was late afternoon on Saturday when dad and I pulled away from the dock. We were amply supplied with minnows and crawlers, and a survival kit of cold ones and chips. The air was still and quiet except for the drone of the trolling motor. It seemed we had the whole lake to ourselves. The scattered wispy clouds gave promise that a sinking Sol would soon be painting a typical northern sunset of pink and orange and bright red.

Sipping from our brew, and chatting about everything and nothing, a father-in-law and son-in-law were bonding. I don't think either of us cared if we caught anything. As the boat plodded southward there were occasional tugs on our lines to remind us we were fishing. Not surprising, no monstrous Pisces made an appearance.

It must have been the combination of a couple brews and the warmth of the afternoon sun that had lulled me into a state of total relaxation. I was genuinely enjoying the serenity of the moment. Maybe angling had some redeeming features.

Without warning, I was rudely brought back to reality by a violent jerk from the lake's depths. Before I could even react, my beautiful rod and reel were disappearing into the murky water. My valiant efforts to retrieve them nearly capsized the boat, but… Damn, they were gone, to forever rest on the lake's muddy floor.

Oh how I wanted to say it was "the Cedar Lake Nessie" that claimed my five foot Shakespeare. Of course, no one would have believed me, most especially my dumb-founded captain watching from the stern. Not a man of many words anyway, Big Al was speechless. All he could reiterate, in consolation, to his klutzy crew mate…" It could have happened to anyone."

And that's the true story of how the "five footer" got away.

P.S. I can't remember ever fishing again.

Lost at Sea...Sorta

We were adrift all right, but not on an ocean. It wasn't even a Great Lake, though Huron was only a quarter of a mile to our east…if only we knew which way was east. The cottage from whence we had departed was about the same distance to our north…if only we knew which way was north.

Now, I'm sure anyone familiar with "the mitten's" sunrise-side, and the area between Oscoda and Greenbush would laugh me out of Iosco County for a claim of being lost on Cedar Lake; but they weren't with us.

Cedar is a gorgeous, heavily treed setting for the myriad of homey cottages that dot its shoreline. While it spans most of the nine miles between the two resort towns, its breadth in most areas would hardly challenge Michael Phelp's back stroke, or Tiger's five wood. You could say it looks like a wide river with not much current.

The Preston cottage sits at the lake's north end where a swamp and springs give it origin. Over the years the cozy bungalow built by the family back in the mid-forties, has been expanded, to include a large pole barn and a boathouse, over the water. Five generations later it remains a haven for pleasure and fond memories.

On a few occasions my sister Carolyn and family would rent a cabin a little to our south, but spend most of the time with us. One memorable day in June was especially disappointing for everyone. The temperature was unseasonably cool for so late in the month. Overhead hung an umbrella of heavy dark clouds that threatened to leak at any moment. It was a day of indoor games and squabbling for frustrated kids, and boring conversation for frayed parents. As evening drew nigh a modicum of clearing tempted Laurie, our oldest, and her cousin Paulie to begin begging to go fishing. The elder Paul and I, as eager to escape as they were, readily acceded.

Fortified with a cold six-pack, we loaded the kids and their gear onto grandpa's home-made fishing boat and set out "to sea." Still ringing in our ears was the stern admonition that supper would be served in forty-five minutes and we'd best not be late.

With a sincere intention of a brief trip, I did not add fuel to the almost empty tank that fed the five horse trolling motor. Young Paul eagerly rowed us to the middle of the lake. Rather than dropping anchor, we let the boat drift in the still water; barely nudged by a very gentle breeze from the north…or so we thought.

The cousins seemed to be having fun in spite of their unsuccessful angling. Paul and I, enjoying our libations, were heedless of the fact that more than an hour had elapsed since our departure. More ominous was our sudden awareness of being enshrouded by the dense fog now blanketing the lake. I dare say even a Londoner would have been impressed. I could barely discern the portly silhouette of my brother-in-law in the bow. The dinghy was not equipped with lights, and we had no flashlights. Cell phones were not yet available. The earlier slight breeze had ceased, leaving us with no clue as to which direction we might be headed. With so little fuel, I was hesitant to use the motor until I was sure we were heading north.

I had been vacationing on the lake since before our marriage so I felt confident if we could find a shore, and I identified any house, I would know if we were on the east or west side of the lake. We could then trace our way north along that shoreline. Once again Paulie began to row.

"I see a light," Laurie yelled with excitement.

When we reached it I had to actually climb ashore and practically touch the structure before I could recognize it. Reasonably sure we were on the west side I dared to use the outboard. The light quickly disappeared into the blackness as I attempted to follow the shore, far enough out to avoid docks, and boats, and rafts. Soon another light emerged from the shore. Once again I climbed out to make sure of our location, only to be dismayed. Like folks lost in a blizzard, we had circled back to the same house. The kids weren't really panicked but we tried to reassure them anyway, a tropical typhoon wasn't likely nor was the possibility of being rammed by some large ship, nor being upended by a frolicking whale, or an attack by sharks. That didn't lessen their concern about going hungry for the hours it might take for the fog to lift, or our dread of the wrath of two angry wives we would eventually face. Now, with even less fuel and more trepidation we slowly resumed our quest for home.

Then, like a divine beacon the stillness of the eve was broken by the resonant clanging sound I recognized as the large bell hanging in the front yard of the cottage. We were indeed heading north. Our absence, now two hours, had aroused Joanne's suspicion of our plight.

The multiple lights of the cottage penetrating the pea soup, were a welcome sight. We had made it. Only after a few laughs and expressions of relief came the scolding and chastisement we were expecting, and a supper of re-heated beans and burgers.

Well, at least we didn't have to clean fish.

"Being a part of the Shiawassee Area Writers group has been a very rewarding and educational experience. Actually being published was an exciting adventure. I couldn't have imagined what it was like, or how awful it would have been to have missed this awesome opportunity." ~ Brenda Stroub

Brenda Stroub is a born again Christian who wants to encourage and share Christ's love to others. She has always enjoyed writing testimonials, personal essays, memoirs, prose, and journaling.

She has been a member of Shiawassee Area Writers for three years and was published in their anthologies: *Winter in the Mitten*, and *Spring in the Mitten.* She is also the Secretary and Publicist for the group.

Brenda was born in Flint, and graduated from Durand High School. She has also lived in Dayton, and now resides in Lennon with her husband, Kip. They have two adult children and ten grandchildren. You can find more about her on Facebook.

Summer Goodbyes

In memory of Dianna Patsey.

Date of birth: 10-20-1957

Date of diagnosis: 07-12-2019

Date of rebirth in Christ: 07-13-2019

Date of transition to Heaven: 09-22-2019

It was a quick, hard summer as I spent time with my sweet neighbor. She had been diagnosed with terminal cancer. It was tough to share her final days, knowing she wouldn't be out in her yard the next summer. Some of her favorite things to do in the summer were floating in her pool, playing with her dogs, and working in her beautiful flower gardens.

When she first received the diagnosis and came home from the hospital, she immediately called me and asked when our friends, Randy and Joyce, would be coming again. Because she knew her time was short, she wanted to get her life right with the Lord. Without delay, I called my husband's best friend, Randy, who is a Preacher in Alma, and his wife, Joyce. They came within hours and we prayed with Diane as she asked to be forgiven of her sins, and placed her life into the Lord's hands. She felt at peace knowing that Jesus would be with her through all the coming circumstances.

Every weekend Diane's daughters and sister came up from Battle Creek. They laughed over pictures and cherished memories, while her husband took care of her every need. Then before we knew it, she was gone. This poem came to me as I pictured her in heaven.

Goodbye my precious neighbor and friend.

Goodbye to the times of laughter over the fence.

Goodbye to the beautiful first cuts of peonies you'd bring.

Goodbye to your sweet compliments and lovely smile.

Goodbye Diane. Goodbye.

"Hello Diane. Hello" -Says Jesus.

"All dressed in white, wearing your crown.

No more pain, no more sorrow.

No more tears for all your tomorrows.

Come on in, I've prepared a place for you.

Welcome home, my daughter. Welcome home."

Summer Acronym

S - Salvation through Jesus Christ is God's

U - Ultimate

M - Mercy

M - Marvelous

E - Eternal

R - Redemption

Summer is a great time to give your life to the Lord and secure your spot in Heaven. It's a season of change, fresh starts, and feeling alive. You can make this a season to remember with new life in Christ. He's only a prayer away. It's as easy as **A, B, C**.

A - Admit you're a sinner. *Rom 3:23 "For all have sinned, and come short of the glory of God."* And *Rom 6:23 "For the wages of sin is death; but the gift of God is eternal life in Jesus Christ our Lord."*

B - Believe. *I John 5:13 "These things have I written unto you that believe on the name of the Son of God; that ye may know that ye have eternal life, and that ye may believe on the name of the Son of God."*

C - Confess. *Rom 10:9 "That if thou shalt confess with thy mouth the Lord Jesus, and shalt believe in thine heart that God hath raised him from the dead, thou shalt be saved."*

Scriptures are from the KJV of the Bible, taken from the public domain.

Summer Essay

Summer of 1970.

On our first day back from summer break of my senior year, our Home Economics teacher asked us to write an essay about our plans after graduation. This would be the easiest essay I'd ever written since I had gotten engaged over the summer. I wrote about our wedding plans. The theme was as long as we had love and each other, we'd get through whatever came along in life. You can imagine how I felt when my teacher wrote on the top of my paper, "*Nice essay, but you can't live on love.*"

Now fifty years later, here is my response.

What I have learned through life so far, is that you can't live *without* love. It's the main ingredient that gets you up everyday and forces you to continue on. You must love someone or something enough to carry you through and give you the drive to exist. Without love people give up, become depressed, and lose hope. You must love and believe to push past the impossible situations in life.

And to go even further with this statement: If God hadn't first loved us enough to send his Son. Who loved us enough to die for us. So we could be forgiven of our sins, and through Him have eternal life. Then we wouldn't have a life at all. So, I have lived on love, and I do believe to this day she got it wrong.

I'm so glad I did not give up on my beliefs and that they have carried me through. And I can say: "*Love bears all things, believes all things, hopes all things, endures all things; love never fails.*"

1 Cor 13:7-8

A binding love is created by a binding faith. The kind of faith that's willing to do whatever it takes and never gives up.

Love finds a way.

Love goes all the way.

Love conquers all.

God is Love.

Summer Love

One bright, summer day, a friend and I were at the roller rink in Durand. Diane introduced me to, Kip, who would soon become the man of my dreams. He asked me to moonlight skate to "Moon River." When he grabbed my hand, I fell in love. That's how it all began.

He looked like the Fonz on "Happy Days." Wearing a black leather jacket, white jeans, and engineer boots. My heart melted.

He asked me out for a date, but I told him I wasn't old enough. I was only fourteen. He flipped me a dime and said, "Call me when you turn sixteen."

I watched him from the bleachers playing football and wrestling. He took 'All-Conference Unanimous Choice' in football and was rated second place in the league for wrestling. He was way out of my reach, but my feelings only grew stronger. He was a jock and I was a bookworm. I couldn't imagine how we would ever get together. But God had a plan.

Soon Kip joined the Navy. During his second tour in the Mediterranean, he sent letters to five girls back home. I was one of the lucky girls. My letters kept coming even after all the others had stopped. He asked me if I'd meet him at the Flint Bishop Airport when he came home on leave just before Christmas in my junior year. My heart thumped extra hard, and my hands were sweaty as I rode to the airport with his dad and step-mom.

Kip and I were together as much as possible in the short time he was home. Before we knew it, we had to say goodbye. When he returned to the ship, he sent me a letter with a picture of him. He said there was a surprise in the picture for me. It was his class ring. I still have this picture in my wallet; it's my favorite.

When he came home on leave the following summer, we'd walk to the ice cream shop and the bowling alley. One time while we were bowling, he wrote on the top of our score sheet, "I Love You." After he walked me home that night, as I stood on the top step of our porch, I turned around to say goodnight. He quickly kissed me before I even knew what happened. I was so overwhelmed by my first kiss, I started to cry and ran inside, straight upstairs to my room.

My mom, who was in the living room with my grandparents, ran up after me saying, "What'd he do to you?" (probably thinking I'd been raped or something) I answered, "He…he…kissed me."

Another special night was my junior prom. My Mom made a beautiful white, empire waist dress, with embroidered red roses on it. I got my hair done at a friend's salon. All swirled up in a beehive style with flowers tucked in, and pretty barrettes to match. He placed a red corsage of baby rosebuds on my wrist and took me to the high school. He taught me to waltz. It felt like I was dancing on air as he whirled me around on the dance floor in his big, strong arms.

One night during the summer of my senior year, he called me from the ship and asked me to marry him. We became engaged over the phone, and he told me to pick out a ring in my dad's jewelry store. On his next leave, he paid for the ring and asked my father for my hand in marriage. Then he proposed traditionally on one knee in the living room. As he placed the ring on my finger, he kissed me, making it all official.

I barely remember my senior year. Before I realized it, I'd graduated and two weeks later we were married, in the summer of 1971. He signed as my legal guardian when I got my first driver's license because I was only seventeen.

It's been over fifty-two years since we met. After two kids and ten grandchildren, we've been married forty-nine years. God worked all things out for the good in our lives. We can now reflect over the journey of our marriage and see His distinctive hand in drawing us together and preserving our love, bound in faith together with Him. We thank God for these blessings and like one of our favorite movies, we can truly say, "It's a wonderful life."

"Last December I attended my first SAW meeting with hopes to shape my general writing skills. My writing inadequacies and insecurities left me vulnerable and exposed. This writing venture with the SAW group has equipped me with valuable applications and tools. I have learned so much about the logistics of becoming a writer and I esteem to write a book some day!" ~ Chelsey Hudson

Chelsey Hudson resides on a quaint homestead miles away from a rural town in Mid-Michigan. She is a jack of all trades but a master of one, Jesus Christ. Gardening, quilting, horseback riding, tennis, flower designing, laughing with friends over a cup of tea and visiting ladies in prison are a few of the many hats she wears from day to day. The hat of a writer is a new fashion statement, like seeing a cute hat at the mall but question if it fits you well enough to buy it. This is her first year as a SAW member.

Her passion in life is to inspire and encourage others to take steps out their comfort zones to seek after truth. Every engaging story has a courageous character that yearns for the victorious end. The grandest stories can be experienced via book form; in black and white or via practical everyday life; in living color.

Chelsey's mission as a writer is to point her readers to the greatest Author ever known, the Creator of The Heavens and The Earth.

"For we know with great confidence that God causes all things to work together as a plan for good to those who love Him, to those who are called according to His plan and His purpose" ~Romans 8:28

The Grand Masterpiece

You don't know the meaning of hard work until you've spent a hot summer day baling hay." Ruth Charis chuckled as she read a quote on a Facebook post, while resting on the couch after a long day at the creamery. "Suffering produces perseverance; perseverance, character; character; hope" were the wise words spoken at a youth gathering days ago.

The reality of these two separate truths enlightened Ruth with fresh insight on the process of building one's character. These were not new concepts for her. Yet they perfectly fit together, comparable to two puzzle pieces finding their perfect match, revealing a glimpse of a grander masterpiece. For Ruth, it was like connecting the first two pieces to start a 500,000 count puzzle and the thought gave Ruth an 'aha' moment.

Ruth grew up on what could be considered a hobby farm, on a corner lot of eight acres. Most corporate farmers would consider it a small potato wanna-be; however, that is not the perspective of her family. Her family could also be considered an example of living in the constant provision of Almighty God.

She knew it was all about perspective. What she saw depended not only on what she looked at, but also on the viewpoint of how she looked at it. In light of this fresh revelation, her perspective radically changed. Instead of seeing the discomforts of hard work and endurance from an earthly perspective, her eyes could see it as the tool to building character from a heavenly perspective. It was a part of a grander masterpiece.

Wow. How have I never comprehended these concepts before? Was Ruth's thoughts, as her gaze came back to the quote on Facebook regarding hard work and baling hay that started the ripple effect of her thoughts. She chuckled again, grinned and thought, *I'd like that statement as a bumper sticker for my blue Chevy S10.* Granted, she'd never been a country girl impressed with the latest tattoo, but it would have a story to tell and be a great conversation starter.

"The animals aren't going to feed themselves," were the urgent words of Ruth's mother.

Gone were the few moments of rest upon the couch. Ruth slid off the sofa to tend to the outdoor chores before dusk. Outside, the fresh outdoor air hit Ruth with delight as she stepped off the wrap-around porch, and made her way toward the hungry rabbits. Usually, these evening chores could be done in her sleep, however, this evening felt somehow different.

Her heart leaped with joy when she heard the peaceful coo from a dove perched on the red barn. This simple dove allowed her gaze to rise up to see the golden rays that penetrated the pink and red clouds. A melodious song of worship found its way to her lips. Her senses awakened in awe with majesty.

Yesterday, she had rushed through her chores, but tonight was different. "What is different about tonight?" Answering her own question, she thought, "My efforts yesterday were merely out of duty and obligation."

With diligence she filled the water bowl for the feline clowder.

Her wheels were spinning and she continued to find herself pondering upon these random thoughts and concepts of enduring through hard work. The realization of individuals her age who had never experienced a task that required blood, sweat and even a few tears, seemed ridiculous.

Ruth thought about a sad reality that may come if her peers were to be socially independent, entitled to the next free handout or shaped by the distractions of pop culture. The life of leisure and self-reliance sounded like a robot without much character. Quick to invent intellectual formulas and find the easiest way out. The satisfaction of working through an obstacle as a team would be lost. Nothing could compare a relationship that's established through accomplishing what seemed like the impossible, together.

Ruth reflected upon the accomplishments achieved during her long days at the Organic Creamery. The Creamery prided themselves on producing the best glass of Mocha milk this side of Michigan, and it was the result of constant teamwork. She thought about her Carhartt jacket that hung on the hook in the basement, it still carried the essence of *fumier de vache* from months ago. The smell of manure lingered upon the fabric, not because it hadn't been washed, but because she wore it as the main source of warmth as she milked and mucked the parlor in bitter cold.

Obviously, not many young adults would value those character building experiences, and to be honest, there were days where she too fell in the trap of resentfulness, to the point of bitterness. As she wrestled with the many challenges, it set the stage for her to understand the reward of nobility within a commitment. Only through the sufficient grace given to her through the blood of Jesus Christ, did it enable her to victoriously get to the other side. Through hard work, Ruth learned to enjoy the less desirable tasks as a valuable quality to one's character.

Ruth walked into the pole barn. Finding the light switch, she gave it a flick, illuminating a path through the stacks of hay, piled to the rafters. She thought about what a great accomplishment it was to have the firmly packed square bales stored in the barn. It was more than a winter's supply of horse feed, because it helped to shape the character and unity of her family.

She thought back to the day her family stacked these bales and once again her senses were overwhelmed with praise and adoration. She knew that only the hand of God could've held back the pouring rain until the last wagon was placed beneath the barn's roof for protection. She could almost taste the refreshing cup of lemonade from that day that had sustained her thirsty body.

She remembered praying that somehow the storm in the west would pass by, without ruining the dry hay scattered throughout the field. She remembered the flashes of lightning that pierced the clouds in the sky, like fireworks. She remembered the adrenaline rush through her aching body, as she tried to mask the pain that screamed from her exhausted muscles.

That had been a day of great victory! The impossible had been accomplished, despite the exhaustion of baling hay eight stacks high on a moving wagon. Ruth had acquired a servant's attitude while she learned firsthand to rest and rely on God in a new and powerful way that would have otherwise been disregarded. She had seen the beauty in allowing God to accomplish the impossible things in life, all while trusting in His perfect timing.

Ruth observed the stacks of hay that could only be explained by God's supernatural provision. She journeyed outside basking in the moonlight among the twinkling stars. She was even able to witness a shooting star to the south. "My heart is overflowing, Lord," were the only words she could audibly speak.

Later on that evening, before falling into a deep restful slumber, Ruth reevaluated all the puzzle pieces she'd discovered that day. They truly revealed glimpses of the grand masterpiece that was taking shape within her life.

It was a journey that was shaping her character. It was the beauty of God's redemptive plan for her life. It was His unrelenting love toward her even when life required endurance. The confidence that she had as she rested her head upon the pillow, could not be explained or defined by her own understanding. For she is His masterpiece!

The Nature of Time

The morning buzz of honey bees hustle and bustle amidst the heavenly aroma of fresh cut alfalfa, before the intense beams of the July sun dries up the entire crop. Busy are the colonies to retrieve a sufficient amount of pollen to sustain them for the upcoming winter food supply. Timing is essential!

The boisterous revving engine of the John Deere tractor makes its final round to complete a task at hand. It provides a fresh new haircut for this three-acre alfalfa field without breaking down or having to be tinkered on. Timing is essential!

The confident words of a local meteorologist rings in the background, giving hope to the farmer. The moisture in the air, for the next three days, will continue to dissipate. Timing is essential!

The child grumbles with complaints, because much is required. These are days that should be spent in the neighbor's pool, not on a wagon shedding blood, sweat and tears while stacking hay bales. Timing is essential!

The sustaining love, grace and mercy is freely offered to all. There is a season, and a time to every purpose under heaven. God made everything beautiful and appropriate in His time. He planted eternity and a sense of divine purpose in every heart, a mysterious longing which nothing under the sun can satisfy, except Him. Yet, who can comprehend or grasp His overall plan, from beginning to the end? Timing is essential!

"SAW authors and writers are friendly and genuine. Members contribute to the group with encouragement in a teaching and training environment. Individual members freely share their experiences and knowledge." ~Carol Inman

I Cor 13:13
Love!
Carol Inman

Carol Inman writes memoirs. She discovered her passion for writing while in high school. Each short story will take you on a journey to a moment in time to share her experience. Things she learned as a child growing up on a dairy and cash crop farm are shared in a teaching style. Her memoirs are historical accounts and written from personal knowledge. She will pull you into her life and captivate you into the story.

Growing up in rural Shiawassee County, she graduated from Corunna High School and received a Business Administration Degree from Baker College. She joined the Shiawassee Area Writers in 2018. She currently lives on a small farm near Bancroft with her husband Wayne. They are the parents of three children. They have three grandchildren and six great grandchildren.

Legacy of Love

Mom and I watched from the living room window as the mailman left a small brown package and a medium size white envelope in our mailbox. Mom had a puzzled look on her face. She had not ordered anything and did not expect a delivery. Items like these were seldom in the mail. Our mailman tapped the car horn "beep beep" to get our attention and to let us know something special had arrived. Eager to learn the content of the two items, I could hardly wait to fetch the mail.

Our mailman, Bill, brought letters and packages from the post office in town to our farm and our neighbors' houses all along the road. In return, he took letters and packages from our farm, to the post office in town. Mail went from there to the address that my mom provided. Mom could ask him to leave postcards and stamps. He would take a package from her to the post office, weigh it, send it, and leave a small brown envelope for payment the next day. He knew all of our family members by first names. Our family trusted Bill, as he was well known for his honesty. Protecting our privacy and remaining honest were two of his best qualities. He took pride in the way he performed his specific work.

I had taken a small envelope to the mailbox earlier that morning. It was my responsibility to take the family's outgoing mail to the mailbox before Bill arrived and to retrieve the mail after he delivered it. This morning, the envelope I put into the box included a note from my mom. "Please leave five, penny postcards and five, two-cent stamps. Thank you." I put the note, one nickel, and one dime in the envelope.

Our mailbox stood at the edge of the road south of our driveway. It stuck about four feet out of the ground, on a four by four post. This allowed Bill the ability to access the mailbox by rolling down his car window and easily putting mail into our mailbox. The height of the mailbox made it impossible for me to see inside. I could stretch my arm up and use my hand to push in the small envelope. On the side of our mailbox was a metal, two-inch by three-inch flag. Dad and I had painted our mailbox white and the flag red. Flag down meant Bill did not have to do anything except leave mail. Flag up meant Bill had something to do for the family. I could reach the flag and push it up with my fingertips. Bill delivered mail on Monday, Tuesday, Wednesday, Thursday, Friday, and Saturday. All mailmen rested on Sunday and did not deliver mail on holidays.

On this August day, Mom sat in her rocking chair in the living room of our big farmhouse with her Bible open on her lap. Every morning at 9:15 a.m., my grandmother joined her to read God's word and pray together. Grandma lived in a tiny mobile home on our property. Dad and Mom made her welcome after Grandpa passed away. I could hear my grandmother's footsteps coming in the back entrance. I counted three steps as she slowly made them one-at-a-time. Physically fragile, she grabbed the handrail to steady herself, just as she had done so many days before. She opened the screen door, stepped inside, and turned slightly to close and latch it behind her. She made her way to her chair in the living room and sat by my mom and the big picture window. Even with her fragility, she had a keen mind, knew many Bible scriptures, and could quote verses from memory. I admired her for believing in the birth of Jesus and her faith in God. I thought of my grandmother as our family pioneer who lived the example of giving great gifts of love and encouraging others to do the same. From their chairs, they could see and observe activity in front of our house.

"The mail's here. Would you bring it in?" Mom called from the living room.

Getting the mail was a fun chore for me. It brought news from family and friends that lived miles away. I looked forward to it. Bill delivered it about the same time each day. Curious and eager to know as to what Bill would leave that day, I ran barefooted out the screen door, letting it slam shut behind me. I ran across the porch and down three steps. My bare feet on the scorching hot concrete sidewalk gave me pause. Stumbling to pick up one foot and then the other, I gracefully danced until I reached the cool shaded grassy lawn. My feet, used to being barefoot, hardly felt the gravel stones as I ran down the driveway. Standing on my tiptoes, I reached in and grabbed the delivered goods.

I held a letter with a birthday seal on the bright, white envelope. Fred and Mina Heath sent it, according to the return address. I recognized Mina's handwriting. The soft squishy envelope had the scent of roses. The brown package said "Happy Birthday, Sis!" written in pink letters just under Mom's name and address. I ran to deliver them to my mom. She would have to wait to open them because her birthday was still two days away.

Grandmother had a saying, "Patience is a virtue. We wait until the day and time." Grandma was a kind, gentle, soft-spoken person. When she spoke, you stopped, listened, and knew that any of her words were not up for discussion. Therefore, we will wait for the birthday and time.

Fred and Mina were friends of my dad's before my parents were married. My dad worked in Flint, Michigan and needed a place to live. He rented a room from Fred and Mina. Soon, Dad married Mom. The friendship between my parents and Fred and Mina grew into a special relationship. Mom and I squeezed the white envelope and tried to guess the content. Grandma observed our curiosity and smiled. We had no idea what was inside the package, but resigned ourselves to wait until after birthday dinner to discover what the package contained.

Mom's sister Marietta and brother-in-law Cloyd sent the brown package. Mom was one of ten children and followed Aunt Marietta in birth order. They always kept in close contact. The package contained something hard. I guessed a box with a pretty shiny decorative pin for Mom's Sunday dress. Mom thought it could be a box of stationary. Mom and her sister wrote letters often. Stationary would be a nice gift. We put the two items on the small round table in the living room and waited for Mom's special day to arrive.

I planned to bake Mom a yellow birthday cake with confectioner sugar frosting and decorate it in pink. She especially liked the color pink. The birthday person got to pick their favorite meal and have it served on a special plate. Mom had chosen roast beef, mashed potatoes and gravy, corn-on-the-cob, homemade bread and butter, coffee, and milk. My dad raised the beef, potatoes, and corn on our farm. Every Saturday, Mom baked bread and churned the butter from the cream and milk from our cows. We used a birthday plate made of fine china with a hand-painted, long-stem, pink rose across the center.

My three married sisters came to help prepare the meal. We set the table with our good place settings and best silverware. Cut pink roses positioned in the center of the table were from Grandma's flower garden. The family members would join us for dinner to honor Mom's day of birth. My grandmother, my brother, and his wife, my three sisters, and their husbands, two aunts, and two uncles would all come to honor this special family time with my mom. Some family members could not attend because of distance. Guests sat around the big table in the dining room. We placed Mom at the head of the table with Grandma on her left and my dad on her right.

"Let us pray. Thank you, Jesus, for this birthday celebration. Help each of us to share the gift of love." Dad gave the prayer blessing. "Teach us to do your will. For you are our God; may your good Spirit lead us on level ground. Psalm 143:10, In Jesus name, Amen." Lively conversations covered various subjects. It had been several weeks since we had seen each other.

Finally, the time came for Mom to open her gifts. Dad asked me if I would do the honors, fetch the gifts one at a time, and present them to the birthday person. Excited, I jumped to my feet ready and willing.

I grabbed the white envelope and hurried to deliver it. When Mom opened letters, she always shook the content to one end and tore off the edge of the other end. Next, she blew into the open end to expose everything inside. She used her forefinger and thumb to pull the items out. Fragrant perfume smell filled the air. The envelope contained a birthday card and homemade hanky. Mina bought white delicate handkerchief material by the yard. She had hand-sewn the edges and crocheted a pink border on all four sides. One corner included a crocheted pink rose with a green, leafy stem. Fred signed the store bought card with a personal birthday message. Mom took a deep sigh and commented. "This hanky is a gift from the heart. She crocheted each stitch with love. I will mail them a thank you."

I retrieved the brown package next and handed it to her. Mom opened it and held a book in her hands. Tears of joy filled Mom's eyes. The name of the book was, *Judy of Rogues' Harbor* by Grace Miller White published by New York Grosset & Dunlap Publishers Copyright, 1918 by The H.K. Fly Company. The author dedicated the book, "Lovingly I dedicate this book to my soldier boy, Bobby, and his brave-hearted comrades 'Over There'." My grandparents gave this book as a gift to Marietta in 1923. The inscription from Aunt Marietta to my mom read, "To Martha, That you may have a happy birthday is the wish of your sister and brother-in-law. Marietta and Cloyd." Aunt Marietta and Uncle Cloyd usually gave a sentimental gift. Mom and Marietta had read this book together over many times when they were young girls. Now, both sisters were married and lived miles apart. Both sisters loved to read this book. Aunt Marietta gave this special gift from her heart. It was now for my mom to keep.

Grandma spoke softly, "It brings tears to my eyes too." She continued, "I am emotional because I know this book has had special meaning to them both. It is special to me too." The ten siblings were taught by my grandparents, work together, play together, and love each other. Love is an action that you take to bring the emotion of love to your heart.

Bill left my mom a birthday card and note in the mailbox. He wrote, "Happy Birthday! Bill." You could count on him to be thoughtful and dependable. Mom received many cards and letters for her to open that day.

Mom thanked everyone with, "How good and pleasant it is when brothers (siblings) live together in unity! For there the Lord bestows his blessing, even life forevermore, Christians will receive blessings if you do not argue. And, I read that in the book of Psalm 133: 1 & 3b."

And to think, that is the legacy Grandma left. Having the family together and giving cards and gifts in person or through the little white mailbox stirs emotion in both the giver and the receiver. Focus on doing for others. Our mailman delivered legacy of love from family, friends, neighbors, and Mom's siblings for her special day. Grandma taught each of us by her example. Throughout my life, I remember the love lessons taught to us by her. Today our family has five generations practicing "Legacy Of Love" and the message "You are special."

"I appreciate SAW for the camaraderie of some wonderful people. After many years of writing alone without sharing my work or being critiqued, SAW gave me that audience of other writers. Sharing and comparing has made a difference in the way I feel about my own writing. I have been inspired and taught by the others in the group as well as being exposed to other genres and opinions." ~Leland Scott

Best Wishes,
Leland Scott
PS 28:7

Leland Scott is an aspiring writer of poetry and short stories. Leland has published three books: *Pangatango's Secrets*, *BASIC DRAFTING a manual for beginning drafters*, and *Special Moments in Poetry,* and is a contributor author to the published books, *Winter in the Mitten* and *Spring in the Mitten.*

Leland is a person of many areas of accomplishment–a retired Navy veteran of 20 years, a college instructor of 22 years, where he was awarded Instructor of the Year award as well as being named the college Poet Laureate, writing a column for a monthly college paper. He is an architectural designer, and is the recipient of several degrees including MBA, BA, teaching certificates, and diplomas from several trade schools.

The Trip Home

Hey Joan, I'm going to Michigan. You wanna go along?"

Startled, Joan looked up and nearly bumped her head on the open hood of the car where she was working, but without hesitation, replied, "Sure! When do we go? Then, just as quickly, added; "How long will we be gone? I need to see if I can get off from work."

As Joan moved away from her task and toward him, Lance's story quickly replayed in her mind. Lance, just discharged from the Navy, was passing through Richland only six months before and had stopped briefly at her father's gas station where they'd met. He decided to stay in town for a while and settled in. He and Joan had become friends and constant companions. She still knew little of his past, but when he shared that he had lived with his grandparents in Michigan one summer as a kid, and never returned, she became curious. She had been concerned about Lance's reluctance to go 'home' to Michigan and had encouraged him to take a trip to reconnect with the grandparents who were the only family he knew. His sudden decision to make the trip surprised her, but the invitation sounded like fun.

"I'll talk to my dad and see if he can spare me for a few days. When do you want to go?"

"Well, I was thinking about today," he stammered, "but I haven't talked to my boss yet, either. I have to go soon–before I lose my nerve–maybe in a few days."

Joan grinned in agreement. She didn't want Lance to change his mind. "Go talk to Judd at the marina, and I will talk to my dad."

Lance quickly jumped in his truck and headed for the marina, his mind racing. He knew he was committed now. If Joan agreed to go with him, he would have to go. He envisioned again the memory of his grandparents' farm in Michigan where he had been one whole summer when he was ten-years-old. He had enjoyed living with his grandparents, and he had gone to their church and became a Christian there–a decision that was a part of him ever since; yet, he had not communicated with his grandparents since. He had returned to Chicago to live with his mother until joining the Navy. She died while he was away and he just never went back to Chicago or to his grandparent's farm. "Maybe Joan is right, it's time."

It was an early morning in mid-June when Lance and Joan finally began the trip. It would take only hours, but seemed like the other end of the world. With an address that Lance hoped was still correct and with their GPS to guide them, they started off. Lance had put new tires on his pickup at Joan's insistence, and he allowed her to check the engine over as though they were going on a wilderness trek.

Joan insisted that they make it a fun trip and not worry about what lay at the end of their journey. "Let's take the back roads." She said, "We can see the world as we go. If we don't find your grandparents, we'll still have a good trip."

Lance agreed and they chattered about the sights they saw as they drove. Joan, who confessed that she had never been fifty miles from home before, was wide-eyed. She began a journal, writing down each town they passed through and commenting on the beautiful vistas of mountains and farmland. Stopping occasionally to explore a yard sale or visit a scenic overview on the road, they made it a trip of adventure. They never mentioned the destination until they saw the "Pure Michigan" sign. They stopped at an Information Center where Joan examined the large map on the wall, looking for the little town of Hindly which was near their destination. Lance said he figured it would be a couple more hours. They both tensed with apprehension.

"Should we call them?" Joan asked. "Can we just show up?"

Lance, now frustrated, rubbed his forehead, "I dunno, but I don't have a phone number. I don't know what else to do."

"Maybe we should have written or something first." Joan ventured.

"It's kinda late now. We didn't plan this very well. Maybe we could stop in town and try to find a phone book or something. We really should find out if they are even still there."

"Right, we should make sure." She agreed.

As they entered the little town, they stopped at a gas station to fill up. Joan went inside looking for a restroom. An older gentleman was leaning on the counter near the door. "I see your out-of-state plates; where you headed?" he asked.

"We are hoping to find Roy and Mary Cooper's farm. " She answered.

"You're close." He replied. "It's only a few miles to the north."

"Do you happen to have a phone book? I'd like to call them before we get there."

"Sure, but you don't need it. I can tell you the number. Do you mind telling me why you're looking for them?

"They're kinda long-lost relatives." She responded.

"Long-lost relatives? How so?"

As she hesitated to say more, Lance entered and she turned toward him and said, "This is Lance Cooper, a grandson."

"Lance?"

"Yes sir."

"Well, I'll be doggoned! They will faint!" He reached out and grasped Lance's hand. "I'm Harold Johnson. Last time I saw you, you were a little snot-nosed kid! You don't remember me, but I remember you in church with them when you were just a little guy. Last I heard, you were in the Navy, right?" Without waiting for an answer he continued, "You head on west a couple miles, take the first dirt road to the right and it's about three miles north. Remember what it looks like?"

"Yes sir. I think so."

"Well, head on out. I'll call 'em and tell 'em you're coming."

Lance and Joan followed Harold's direction and found the 'dirt road' and turned.

"That's it!" Lance exclaimed. "That's the church!" He slowed for a moment, then continued on, pointing out things that he remembered. Suddenly Lance began to smile when he spotted the big red barn and the old farmhouse of his grandparents. His grandparents were waiting on the porch, and hurried out to greet them as they drove into the driveway.

"Lance? Is it really you?" was all his grandmother could say as she reached to hug him. She repeated it over again and again amid tears and laughter before letting him go. His grandfather reached out a calloused hand to Lance's and grinned, speechless.

Lance introduced Joan to them, and Grandma quickly invited them in. "Come inside. You must be starved. When have you last eaten? We just ate supper, but there's plenty left. Come in, Come in." Grandpa followed up the steps and into the house. She led them through the living room into a large kitchen, instructing them to sit as she hurried to fix something.

Grandpa sat down at the end of the table and began to ask questions–wanting to know everything at once. "So you saw Harold? He called and said he saw you. Where have you been all these years? What was it like in the Navy? I'm sorry about your mother. Where are you heading now? Wait till you see the farm, how it has changed. Remember the old John Deere? We still have lt. But we got a new tractor a few years ago. You'll have to see it. No cows anymore. That business kinda dwindled when the big dairies moved in; just crops now. We still have a couple pigs and the chickens. We'll take a walk in the mornin."

Grandma, pushed two plates across the table. "It ain't much–just chicken an' dumplins that we had for supper–and there's half a cherry pie!"

Joan protested, but to no avail. Grandma was insistent.

As they ate, the room grew quieter. Everyone seemed to have run out of words and sat awkwardly looking at one another. Lance began to drink in the atmosphere that was somehow reminiscent of a long time ago. Joan sat quietly, wondering what to say next. She had expected some kind of reunion, but now there was nothing to say. She looked to Lance as if to prompt a conversation.

He finally broke the silence. "I have been meaning to get in touch with you. I was glad to see you at the funeral. I couldn't stay–had to get back to my ship; and then when I got out of the Navy, I was headed across country, no place to go, y'know? I stopped in Richland, met Joan and have been there ever since. I work in a marina part-time. When I told Joan about you, she insisted that we come visit."

That broke the silence. Grandma brought coffee for everyone and they talked for an hour. Grandma told how they had prayed for Lance every day and worried about him, but didn't know how to connect with him. Grandpa talked of the farm and all the memories of the summer when Lance was there. Joan mentioned Grandpa's poems that Lance had shared with her.

"You like them?" Grandma asked. "There's more if you want to read them. He used to write a lot. Not so much anymore. I'll show you some tomorrow."

Suddenly, it grew quiet again and then Grandma began to share. "It was hard knowing of you and not being able to be part of your life, Lance. When John, our son. . .your dad, left home, he was kinda like the prodigal son. He went to Chicago and we just lost him. He never called or anything. Then he married your mother. She called us once in a while. When John was killed in an accident, she let us know.

"What about my sister? I remember a big sister. . ."

"No, that was just a friend of your mother's that stayed with you a while to help her take care of you when you were little."

"When your mother lost her job and asked us to take you for that summer, it was like getting our son back. We invited her to come too, but Chicago was all she knew. She wanted to raise you there by herself. She did call once in a while. She bragged on you when you went in the Navy. We just didn't keep in touch very well. I'm sorry."

"I never knew any of that. I didn't know my dad. I guess I knew that you were his parents, but it didn't make sense. I didn't know what happened. Mom never told me. I got your Christmas and birthday cards. I wondered why we didn't come back to visit or nothing, I just accepted it all. We never went anywhere. We just lived in that old apartment. Then I joined the navy to see what the world was like. I kept the Bible you gave me. I read it all the time. That was good for me; but I never felt like I had a family. Mom wrote to me, but never told me she was sick. I came as quick as I could when I got the message of her death, but that was such a fast trip, it didn't seem to mean much. I'm sorry we didn't get a chance to talk there."

"I'm sorry too."Grandma said. "I'm glad you could be there. We took care of everything. Her ashes are here—so's John's. We kept them together."

"Thanks. I guess you're all the family I've got. Joan convinced me to come talk to you. I hope it was all right."

"Of course it was all right!" Grandpa responded. "You're always welcome here."

"We never forgot you." Grandma chimed in.

They talked on into the evening, then, "You must be tired." Grandma finally offered. "We can talk more in the morning." She led them upstairs to a guest room for Joan, and Lance to his 'old room'.

Morning for Lance brought sounds from the kitchen. He found Joan and Grandma getting acquainted over coffee. They were reading some of Grandpa's poems. "I like this one!" Joan exclaimed, and read aloud,

I love the days of summer
when time slows on the farm
the cattle in the pasture

the earth all green and warm

Forgotten, snows of winter

and dismal springtime rain

replaced by rows of rustling corn

and waves of golden grain

The chirping of a robin

nested in the apple tree

and garden flowers blooming

to tempt the honey bee

All speak of God's creation

that works in harmony

providing and refreshing

in perfect company

And then another:

The aging barn stands stately tall

A monument to time

Fading paint, an empty shell

faint picture of its prime

If weathered boards could speak aloud

they'd tell about the past

relating storms and blazing sun

how they through it all did last

keeping livestock safe and warm

and fed from lofts of hay

those selfsame lofts a place of fun
where young boys went to play

Standing strong for many years
the barn was many things
But now forlorn it merely tells
the mem'ries that it brings

Lance saw his grandpa outside through the window and went to join him. Together they began a tour of the farmyard, past the chicken house and the pigpen, to the tool shed. Grandpa showed him the 'new' tractor–a big difference from the old one which was sitting next to it. They walked through the cow barn, now eerily empty and unused, up to the also empty haymow where Lance had played as a kid.

"It's kinda sad." Lance said.

"Yeah, the barn isn't what it used to be. We still cut some hay, but it doesn't come into the barn anymore—it's out there in those rows of bales along the fence. We sell it to horse people mostly. Things are different in farming than they used to be. You can see the corn and wheat around us where it used to be pasture. That's where the money comes from now."

The two settled into chairs on the back porch in the warm summer sun and shared memories of the past.

Three days passed as Lance continued his reacquaintance with his grandparents. Lance showed Joan some of the places he'd played as a kid. He gave her a ride down the lane on the old John Deere; and on Sunday morning, they visited the little white church where Lance was showered with greetings from older people who remembered 'little Lance'.

The time passed too quickly but Lance and Joan reluctantly decided that they needed to get back to Richland. After, much hugging, and tearful good-byes, they climbed back into the truck for their trip.

"It was nice to meet you." Joan called, waving copies of poems that Grandma had given her.

"I'll be back." Lance called as he backed out of the drive. "Soon!"

As they drove back down the dusty dirt road, Joan tuned to Lance. "Can I come back with you?"

"My SAW peers inspire me to dabble outside of my comfort zone." ~ Lauren George

Lauren George has been writing for herself since childhood. She joined the Shiawassee Area Writers Group to gain insight into the complex world of publishing. What she discovered was a group of knowledgeable writers as talented as they are kindhearted. Lauren currently resides in Byron. When not writing she can be found spending time with her family, exploring nature, meditating, or hiding behind the pages of a good book. This is her second publication.

Lizard Leash

You guys want to hear something funny?" Eloise smiled at her friends.

It was a muggy Michigan Fourth of July. Eloise and her husband Allen were enjoying the company of a few close friends as they sat around the backyard fire pit. Jacob and Alice, their two young children, were busy twirling sparklers through the air. The sky was clear and black, punctured only by starlight, the perfect night for a story.

"Did I ever tell you about that leash I made?" Eloise studied Shalene, Chris, and Grant. "For the lizard we used to have."

Shalene chuckled. "You made what?"

Chris joined in, "Did you just say, you made a leash for your lizard?" He draped an arm around Shalene. "I've gotta hear this."

"Wait, wait, wait." Everyone turned toward Grant, a giant ginger-haired man. He'd dragged his chair away from the fire, to escape the heat. "How did *you,* of all people, end up with a lizard?" Grant raised his eyebrows as if questioning the validity of her story. "I thought you hated them."

"Well, they're not exactly my favorite…" Eloise began.

"We don't have to keep it for long," her husband Allen whispered. "Fred will be back in a few weeks; I'll take care of it."

Eloise rolled her eyes. They both knew that as the stay-at-home parent, the responsibilities would fall on her shoulders.

"It's not that. I can manage a few weeks, but that cage is *filthy*." She frowned at Allen. "Why do people get animals they have no intention of caring for?"

She glanced out the backdoor window. Fred, her husband's acquaintance, struggled to spray what appeared to be a few months' worth of lizard poop out of a large glass tank. "I mean seriously, I hate lizards, but *nothing* deserves to live like that." She gestured towards the door. "Surrounded in your own feces." She sighed, "Okay, I'll help him out. I'll take care of it while he's gone. Under one condition."

Allen eyeballed her from across the kitchen, "Okay, what's your condition."

"We keep it." Eloise could hardly believe the words that were coming out of her mouth. "I can't in good conscience give it back to him. Not when it's obviously being neglected."

"Well honey, it's not ours to take." Allen stood on tiptoe, peering over her head and out into the yard. "Do you really want that thing?"

"No, of course not." Eloise followed his gaze, "but I feel bad for it."

"I can't promise he'll give it to you." Allen shrugged.

Eloise however, had a feeling Fred would be happy to rid himself of the responsibility. "Let me talk to him."

"Oh, I don't know." Fred feigned reluctance.

Eloise decided to give him an easy out. "Well, I just think it will be hard on my kids if we bring it in and they get attached to him. You know, then we give it back. It's sort of confusing for them."

"Oh," he beamed. "I guess I didn't think about that. You really think they'll get attached?"

No, none of us will get attached. I just feel sorry for the darn thing. Eloise thought. "Most likely," she glanced over at the lizard, "It *is* pretty cute." *Cute like a snake with legs.*

"Well, ok, I guess." Fred shrugged, "I'll walk you through what you need to do. He's pretty easy to care for."

Mr. Lizard, as the children dubbed him, did turn out to be easy to care for. Eloise grew accustomed to handling him, each time her palms grew moist less, until they eventually stopped sweating altogether. She enjoyed teaching the kids about bearded dragons and liked to watch him munch on his dinner. She kept his cage clean, gave him weekly baths, and filled his belly. Mr. Lizard was living in the lap of luxury.

"Whatcha' doin' mama?" Her son, Jacob, asked as he entered her room.

"Oh, just watchin' Mr. Lizard eat."

"He's pretty cute." Her son chimed.

"I'm starting to think so too." She admitted.

Her daughter bobbed into the room, pigtails swaying left and right with each step. "I wanna go outside mama."

Jacob jumped up and down, "Can we take Mr. Lizard outside

with us?"

Eloise watched the lizard as he sunned himself beneath the heat lamp. She wished she could take the poor creature outside too. *Well why can't you?* She had an epiphany. Why not let him feel the *real* sun on his back? Surely, she could fabricate a miniature leash. It couldn't be that hard. She could give the lizard a taste of freedom and teach the kids about kindness towards animals. It was a win-win situation.

"You know buddy," Eloise said. "Maybe we can take Mr. Lizard outside."

"*Really?*" Her daughter squealed.

"Sure, why not?" Eloise imagined them walking along the sidewalk, Mr. Lizard leading the way, relishing in his freedom. "I'll just need to make a leash. We don't want him to run off." Eloise envisioned a simple design, a sock with a few arm holes, and some thin twine. Easy enough to slip him into and the leash wouldn't be too heavy. *Easy as pie.*

Eloise grabbed one of her daughter's socks and cut a slit up the back. She poked two sets of holes on either side of the slit, one set on the top and one set on the bottom. She laced some twine through each hole and tied them into a knot. Estimating where the lizard's legs would poke through, she made a few openings to slide them in.

She plucked Mr. Lizard from his prison and slipped him inside the harness. Eloise was both surprised and pleased at how well the design fit. Holding the lizard in her arms she headed to the backyard with her usual entourage of two small children, an eight-month old mutt and her calico cat, Maude.

The summer sun warmed her skin. "Ok guys, let's see how it works." She set the lizard down and waited for the exploration to begin.

"He's not doin' anything." Her son observed.

"I think he likes it." Her daughter knelt and touched the lizard's tail. With a flash he darted into the yard, taking the slack out of the leash.

Wow, he's a lot faster than I thought he'd be. Eloise glanced nervously at the kids. *Hope this wasn't a bad idea.* She gave the leash a tug. The bearded dragon settled on the grass. Eloise frowned. She felt slightly less confident in her leash fabricating skills.

"Mommy, why's he turning black?" Her son asked as he approached the lizard, kneeling to examine him.

"Mmm, I don't know." She worried the creature would nip at Jacob. "Maybe give him some room." She waived the kids back to her. "He's probably scared."

Eloise had all but forgotten about the puppy that accompanied them outside until Mable found her way to Mr. Lizard, giving him a gentle sniff.

"Awww mommy, look at Mable, she's giving him kisses." Her daughter cooed.

The lizard was not only turning black now, but it was drooling. *Oh boy, I've never seen it do that before. This can't be good.* Eloise patted her legs and whistled for the pooch to come.

When Mable lifted her head, to glance at Eloise, all hell broke loose. Without warning the lizard jumped at Mable and clamped down on the puppy's chest. Mable yelped.

"*Mommy!*" the kids screamed as Mable whimpered.

Eloise pulled on the leash hoping to pry the lizard away. Instead, Mr. Lizard latched on deeper, all four of his legs suspended in the air, like a demented flying squirrel. Eloise yanked harder, causing one of the knots to come undone. The leash began to unravel. *Oh boy, I did not think this through.* Her mouth began to feel dry.

The children looked horrified. Eloise *was* horrified. She froze. She knew the only way to grab the lizard now would be with her bare hands. *Oh my god, oh my god. I do not want to touch that thing right now.* Her palms began to sweat, she grimaced in fear. *Stay calm,* she scolded herself, *you're going to traumatize the kids.*

Too late.

Alice and Jacob screamed at the tops of their tiny lungs. Mable shook her body as if getting a bath. The lizard, holding on for dear life, twirled around, like tassels on a topless dancer. Eloise gasped in disbelief as the scene unfolded before her eyes. Mr. Lizard, now free from his leash, was flung into the air. He landed with a plop holding a mouth full of Mable's black fur. Everyone stopped screaming and no one moved.

Do something! Quick! She yelled at herself from deep inside. "Come're Mable." Eloise whistled again. She feared the sweet pup would feel the need to further investigate her attacker. However, one run-in with the creature seemed to be enough. She hustled to Eloise, tail hung low, pupils dilated with fear. Mable dashed in the house as soon as Eloise opened the door.

Eloise returned her attention to the children. Alice was on the verge of tears, Jacob's jaw hung open, his eyes wide. "Maybe you guys should go sit at the table." Eloise was about to usher them off when Alice screamed.

"Mommy look!"

Mr. Lizard was almost all black now. His beard was flared and, as he snapped his head to and fro, a steady line of spit followed. Eloise was reminded of a venom-spitting dinosaur she'd once seen in a movie. *Oh, boy, how am I gonna catch this thing?* She took a few steps in the lizard's direction, trying to keep her cool. The creature, sensing her approach, darted to the back of the yard. Eloise squealed, as he zipped past her, scaring the kids. *Steady.* She tried to calm herself, but she couldn't slow her heartbeat.

Near the edge of the yard, she spotted a tiny opening in the privacy fence, just big enough for the lizard to slip through, if it tried. She needed to think fast. The lizard was only a few feet away from getting more freedom than it ever bargained for. If it got out, the creature would be gone for good.

Eloise noticed movement from the corner of her eye. Their cat, Maude, sat slyly on the fence, observing the situation, growing ever more curious about the lizard by the minute. *Oh no. Watch out Maude.*

The cat slunk down the fence, landing between Mr. Lizard and his hole to freedom. Her body language suggested she was neither threatened nor impressed by the two-foot long lizard frothing at the mouth. Taking advantage of the lizard's frantic head snapping, Maude inched closer until the creature stiffened.

A puddle of drool flowed from Mr. Lizard's mouth as he hissed at the cat. They stared each other down. The lizard puffed its beard to frighten her. Maude, with more moxie than a tiger, called his bluff and stuck her nose right in front of him, as if to say, "Go ahead, tough guy. You've got one shot." *Oh my god, its' going to attack the cat.*

Only Mr. Lizard didn't attack the cat. It seems Mother Nature blessed all her creatures with the good sense to avoid any animal with built in blades. Quick as a flash, the lizard turned and darted toward the center of the yard, scaring Eloise. *Get ahold of yourself. It's not an alligator.*

Thinking about alligators reminded her of a documentary she'd recently watched with the kids. The show featured an alligator farm in the south and explained how the wranglers handled gators by tossing blankets or shirts over their eyes to disorient them. *That's it!*

Eloise scanned the yard for something to cover Mr. Lizard's eyes. Living in a busy neighborhood, she wasn't about to remove her shirt, opting instead to grab an overgrown dandelion leaf from along the fence. Creeping up behind the lizard, a step at a time, she knew she had one shot to catch him. Swallowing hard she bent over, careful not to cast her shadow over him. Afraid to breathe, she swooped down over the lizard, dropping the oversized leaf onto its head. Prepared to abandon the mission and run screaming for the door, Eloise waited for Mr. Lizard to dart out at her. Instead the creature hunkered down to the ground and remained motionless. Eloise suspended her hand over the lizards back, just below its head. She took a deep breath and snatched him up.

"Open the door!" She yelled at Jacob. Running, she held Mr. Lizard at arm's length, praying she could get him back inside the cage without additional incident. Eloise jumped over the threshold, darted past the kids, into her room, and dropped the lizard in his cage. *Note to self, never do that again.*

"Oh my god, you're such a hippy." Shalene was doubled over in laughter, barely able to catch her breath.

"I can't believe you did that." Chris shook his head, as he wiped tears of laughter on his shirt.

Eloise smiled so hard her cheeks hurt.

"I guess I know why you were so chipper after it died." Allen winked.

"Yeah," Eloise admitted. "I wasn't exactly sad to see him go."

"I think we ought to patent your leash design." Grant, always ready with the one-liners, spoke up from the background. "There's gotta be other hippies out there that want to take their lizards for a walk."

"Ya know Grant, maybe I will." Eloise gave the fire a poke. "And when I'm a millionaire, I'll send you one for Christmas."

It was a good night. A wonderful fourth of July, and great story worth retelling.

"I thought I was a writer before I joined SAW – but I was horribly mistaken! With each meeting comes another lesson on how to write more effectively and avoid bad habits in writing style. We also share ideas on how to market our books and stories. When I am in the room with 20 other writers I feel as if I am with a group of friends who share a similar passion. We laugh at our mistakes and we help each other improve." ~Doug Cornell

Douglas Cornell is the author of two novels, *Plastpocalypse* and P*lastipocalypse, Book II: The Barrens.* While both books offer exciting post-apocalyptic thrills, the stories also explore mankind's tendency towards violence and racism. In addition to the novels, Doug has been published in two anthologies, *Winter in the Mitten* and *Spring in the Mitten.* Doug is currently working on his third novel.

When he's not writing, Doug enjoys backpacking and bicycling with his wife, Carol. He also plays a mean guitar in the band The Dirt Surfers.

To see what Doug's up to, follow him at facebook.com/ dirtkahuna.

The Bicycle Thief

Harry Freeman struggled to pay attention. Even though his view outside was partially obscured by the wild hair of the girl that sat beside him, he could see clear blue sky over the city of Owosso. Stretching his legs, he kicked the chair of a huge dude who was directly in front of him, which earned Harry a nasty scowl.

"Sorry man," Harry whispered.

The instructor droned on about x and y and greater than and lesser than and integers. Stuff no human being would ever need to know at any future time in their life. Unless you were going on to be a computer programmer or rocket scientist–and Harry was not exactly on the road to a lifetime of higher education and lucrative employment.

It was obvious, way back in the third grade that Harry would not be aiming for Valedictorian. With a mother who worked 20 hour days and a father that was God knows where, Harry was left to fend for himself. He made his own meals (such as they were, mostly consisting of mac and cheese or PB&J) and spent his free time playing "Call of Duty" on his best friend Pete's Xbox. Harry always figured he'd either end up in the Army or in some dead-end job.

For the time being, he was stuck in Pathways, a special summer school program for troubled youths. As a result of having virtually no parental supervision, Harry had been picked up twice by the local PD for mostly harmless activities. Everyone knows the cops hate skateboarders, so it was no surprise when he was dragged into the office of the Chief of Police after his board accidentally cracked the front window of Dr. Bishop's downtown dentist office. The Chief read Harry the riot act and threatened to come down on him hard if he was ever brought in again.

Harry played it cool through the first two years of high school, but toward the end of eleventh grade he was caught spraying graffiti on the underside of the Main Street Bridge. It didn't matter that the paint belonged to his buddy Pete or that Harry was just embellishing the "art" had been sprayed by someone else. He was the one found holding the can, so he was the one punished.

The Chief and Harry's mother decided Harry would enter the Pathways Program. He'd attend summer school and finish his senior year with a class of other "disadvantaged" students. Harry thought the deal was total crap, but at least he wasn't in a youth detention facility.

As the instructor continued the Algebra class, Harry felt his phone vibrate. He'd long ago figured out how to send covert text messages while in class, so he wasn't the least bit worried about getting caught. It was Chelsea, a girl he worked with part-time at Meijer.

Chelsea: *Meet me at my house at noon?*

Harry: *What about your old man?*

Chelsea: *He's at work*

Harry: *I only have one hour for lunch*

Chelsea: *Then you'd better hurry*

The two of them became friends while they worked the lots at the store, hauling shopping carts left behind by customers. Up to now they'd only flirted, and the one time he went to her house he caught nothing but stink eye from Chelsea's father. Still, this might be an opportunity to go further in their relationship. Looking at the clock, he saw he'd have to endure another hour of class before breaking for lunch.

Harry sprinted across the parking lot and headed for the river trail, which would be the fastest way to get to Chelsea's house on the other side of town. As he ran under the Main Street Bridge, he couldn't help but notice the faded remnants of his graffiti. Smiling, he sprinted up the steep incline and suddenly realized he was not in good enough physical shape to run such a distance. All of the hours playing video games had done nothing for his endurance.

He put his hands on his knees and fought to catch his breath. After a moment he felt better and continued towards Chelsea's house. Passing a small city park, Harry spied a bicycle laying unprotected in the grass. It was one of those fancy racing bikes–the kind that weighs something like 12 pounds. Without a second thought, Harry jumped on the bike and took off. Right away he discovered that the seat was not actually designed to sit on. It was like trying to balance on the blade of a sword! He stood and pedaled, but the machine required maximum effort to go at even a snail's pace.

"Where are the stupid shifters?" he wondered as he plodded

up the path. Eventually he crested the rise and headed downhill, where he picked up momentum and actually began to believe that the bike would be faster than walking.

Covered in sweat, he reached Chelsea's house five minutes later.

"Come on inside," she said, greeting him on the front porch with a come-hither smile.

It was all Harry could do to contain his teenage hormones. Maybe today was the day he'd…

🚲 🚲 🚲 🚲 🚲

Two hours later he jumped from the couch and exclaimed, "Holy crap! I'm supposed to be in English class right now!"

It turned out Chelsea had nothing more in mind than listening to music and playing video games. Losing track of time, Harry simply forgot he was legally obligated to be in the Pathways classroom. The alternative was not at all attractive, as he'd heard stories about the bad stuff that happened at the youth detention center.

Running from the house, he re-mounted the bicycle and headed back towards school. The bike still required all of Harry's strength to move. Stopping, Harry looked all over the machine for the shifters. He'd ridden multi-speed bikes before, but this one was different. Not finding any shifting mechanism, he reached down and forced the chain onto a different gear. Remounting, he was finally able to pedal even though the chain continued to rattle and clank.

As he pedaled through the small park where he'd originally "found" the bike, a voice bellowed: "Stop thief!"

Without thinking, Harry stopped. It never occurred to him to race away to evade arrest.

Two men ran towards Harry. One was dressed in a blue uniform of the local PD. The other wore the clothes of an office worker: dress pants, shirt, and tie.

"What are you doing on my bike?" the office worker demanded.

A wave of anxiety ran though Harry's veins. His hands became cold and his throat closed so tight all he could whisper was, "*Your bike?*"

"That's right! It was locked in my van all afternoon."

The police officer, who wore a name tag "Jenkins," was one Harry hadn't seen in his previous scrapes with the law. "Where did you get this bike?"

Stammering, Harry explained he found it laying in the grass.

"That's impossible," the office worker said, turning to the cop. "It was locked in my vehicle. I was planning on riding right after work."

"But I found it lying beneath that tree…" Harry pointed at the exact spot where he'd discovered the bicycle.

Officer Jenkins moved in closer to Harry's face and said, "I need to see some identification."

Handing over his school ID card, the officer wrote on a

notepad, muttering, "Harry Freeman. Owosso Public Schools."

"Freeman?" The office worker interrupted. "Is your dad Billy Freeman?"

"No sir, Billy's my uncle."

"I went to school with Billy. We were good friends, even though he wasn't exactly from my crowd…"

The office worker paced, thinking. Harry watched the man scratch his head and come to some sort of conclusion.

"This bike cost over $3000 dollars,"

Harry gasped. "Oh my God…"

"That's right, son," Jenkins replied. "This is grand theft." Turning to the office worker, he asked, "What do you want to do?"

The man sized the boy up. He noticed Harry's greasy hands. "You couldn't shift it, could you?"

Pointing at the drive train, he explained to Jenkins and Harry that the bike had been left in its hardest gear. "The shifters are right here, "he said, "Hidden under the brake levers."

Harry felt like a moron. He wasn't even smart enough to shift a bicycle.

The office worker asked Harry, "You said you found the bike lying in the grass?"

"Yes sir. It was right over there. I borrowed it so I could go see my girlfriend."

Chuckling, the man replied, "I see. It doesn't look like anyone broke into my van. I guess it's possible I forgot to lock the doors, or maybe someone else took the bike first and couldn't figure out how to ride it." Thinking for a moment, he asked, "Are you still in school?"

"Yes sir. I'm in Pathways."

"Oh, I've heard of that. It's a special program for kids who have been in and out of trouble."

Turning to the officer, the man asked, "Has Mr. Freeman had any previous run-ins with the law?"

"I've only been in Owosso for a few months. This is the first time I've met Mr. Freeman."

"Mr. Freeman," the office worker said, "How long until you graduate?"

"I'm going into my senior class this year. I should be done next spring."

"Do you understand you've committed grand larceny?"

Harry's eyes filled and he began to sob. "I'm sorry. I had no idea."

"Here's the deal," the man continued. "Because of my friendship with your uncle Billy, I won't press charges."

With a deep sigh of relief, Harry cried, "Thank you!"

The man held up his hand. "I'm not finished. I will be watching you. If you get in trouble again or fail to graduate next year, you *will* go to jail."

Tuning to the officer, the man asked, "I can press charges any time, right?"

"Yes sir. There really isn't any statute of limitations on this sort of thing."

Harry didn't know if this was true or not, but he was extremely grateful. "I promise. I'll stay out of trouble and graduate!"

"You do that," the man said, and he turned away, pushing his bicycle toward his van.

Officer Jenkins shook his head and chuckled. "I've never seen anyone just walk away from a theft where the perpetrator was caught holding the goods. You are a very lucky young man."

🚲🚲🚲🚲🚲

"You, in the back…" As Harry looked at his class roster to find the boy's name, he had a flashback to his own troubled teenage years. *Where would I be now if I hadn't been forgiven for stealing the bike?*

"Mr. Cooper," Harry said. "If you expect to graduate from this program, you'll have to pay attention."

The young man, who'd been daydreaming, sat up in his seat and said, "Who, me?"

"Yes, you. I know it's nice outdoors, but Summer School is the price you pay for screwing around during the regular school year."

The young man's face reddened. "Sorry, Mr. Freeman. I was thinking about a girl."

Prov. 16:24
Connie LaMee

"Connie has been a member of the Shiawassee Area Writers since October 2018. This group of inspiring writers has taught her that she can write, she can rewrite, she can edit, and she can be an author.

Connie is published in the anthology Spring in the Mitten. Under the leadership of Elizabeth Wehman, Connie has gained knowledge and skills that continue to give her confidence. She particularly enjoys writing poetry. Her role model and mentor would have to be Leland Scott. He is a great example of a man who loves God. He has a gentle and kind spirit that taught Connie to write from her heart or there is no story." ~ Connie LaMee

Connie LaMee is a retired preschool teacher from Congregational Child Development Center and St. Joseph Child Care Services. She received her Child Development Associates Degree from Lansing Community College. Her inspiration for writing comes from the true authors of children. Connie kept a collection of crazy, wonderful, funny and precious things that kids would say in her classroom and created a memory book along with photos to present to every child at the end of each year.

"Grammy" rings music to her ears from her six grandchildren. She continues to keep a journal of their stories. Connie resides in Owosso, Michigan with her very supportive husband, Gary. They have two adult children.

God is good! After forty years, Connie was reunited with a SAW member, Brenda Stroub, who sparked her interest in this group of inspiring writers and became a member in October 2018.

The Invigorating Ride

Over forty years…it never gets old
Together we arrange this time worth gold

We head up north, bikes on the rack
On our pick-up truck towards the Mighty Mac

No radio, just the peaceful sound
Of silent praise as we head Northbound

Greeted by the pure Great Lakes
Escorted by the ferry who takes

Our bikes along with us to ride
Mackinac Island on the other side

Upon arrival, we smile and kiss
An extraordinary feeling this marital bliss

Peddling our bikes in fashionable style
We ride with gusto, mile after mile

There's something about that beautiful view
Only our Creator forms colors of blue

Playful waves splash over rocks
High stepping horses go clip clop

Time for a stop along the roadside
Breathtaking views magnified

Skipping stones, a photo shoot
Wading in water together barefoot

Summer time is now complete
Eagerly waiting to repeat

The invigorating eight- mile ride
On the Island side by side

A Schwinn at Seven

It was a scorching, sultry July day, and everyone was glistening with beads of sweat. But that didn't discourage people from engaging in the competitive games which included watermelon seed spitting contests, tricycle races, horseshoe throwing, kickball, water balloons, and corn hole. I participated in the tricycle race until my legs shook.

My niece, Kathy Lynn and her husband, Jerry, delight in throwing family gatherings at their place in the country. My siblings Martha, Kathy, Roger, Lois, Pam, and Tim had already made their way to cool off under the huge old oak tree.

Kathy yelled, "Sister, come over here and sit in the shade with us."

I wobbled my way over to an empty lawn chair and plopped down as Pam handed me a glass of refreshing cold tea.

Martha chuckled, "Connie, you gave it your all in that tricycle race!"

Roaring with laughter, Lois added "Do you remember when Roger and I taught you how to ride a two-wheeler when you were seven?"

Chugging down a gulp of tea, hand over my mouth hoping not to spray anyone as I nodded, tight lipped.

Our youngest brother, Tim burst out, "I don't remember that!"

I smiled, "That's because you weren't born yet."

"Well, then," Tim asked in a humorous tone, "How did you learn to ride a two-wheeler, sis?" Just then Tim's eyes shifted to his four-year-old granddaughter, Addy, riding her two-wheeler with training wheels in the driveway. "Did they have training wheels back when you were a kid, Connie?"

I shrugged. "I don't know, but that's *not* how I learned!" As I began my story, Tim listened intently, his eyes darted between our faces so he wouldn't miss a thing.

We lived in a two-story, white house on Wackerly Road in Midland, Michigan. The house sat off the road up a long driveway. The ditch was deep (well, for a seven year old anyway). We had a small front yard and a big backyard with a creek behind it. Grandma and Grandpa Tripp lived next door. Dad even made a path to their house with his Ford Tractor.

Kathy interrupted my story by adding, "I have that old tractor now."

I nodded, but continued. Roger and Lois were always looking for an adventure so they decided to teach me how to ride Roger's twenty-six-inch bike with a horizontal crossbar.

I was in the driveway pedaling the little red tractor when Lois called to me, "Do you want to learn how to ride a big bike?" I jumped off the tractor, ran to her and Roger as they stood at the top of the ditch with his two-wheeler. Roger held the handlebar with one hand and the seat with his other. Lois stood on the opposite side.

The siblings all snickered. Tim gasped, "Oh no, I can only imagine what happened."

I was ready! Lois lifted me up and told me to straddle my legs over the bar while Roger held the bike steady. He told me to grab the handlebars with my hands and put each foot on a pedal. Then he said, "When we let go of you, push that right pedal hard, then the left and keep pedaling." He also reminded me that I already knew how to pedal from the little red tractor.

"Are you ready to try this little sister?" Lois asked.

"Yup, let's go…" before I could finish the word go, I found myself in the grassy ditch that cushioned my twisted body. Oh the pain from that bar! I recalled. I got right back up and tried again and again until I mastered my new skill. Skinned knees, bruised arms and all! The feeling of coming up the other side of the ditch, into the yard, down the driveway was quite an accomplishment.

Dad had been watching us while he was picking strawberries at Grandpa's next door. He came up to me and said, "I saw you crash a few times. Are you okay?" I told him yes, but it was worth it because now I could ride a two-wheeler.

"Speaking of strawberries," Tim shouted to his granddaughters who were also riding their bikes like we'd done so long ago. "Hey Addy, will you please bring me a piece of that fresh strawberry pie?" She jumped off her bike and ran to the dessert table. She asked her older sister, Charlee, to help carry paper plates and plastic forks as she balanced the whole pie in her small hands to Grandpa Tim.

"My mom made this so I want everyone to have some," Addy bragged. Their mom, Britney, noticed the girls serving everyone under the tree. She walked across the lawn to where we were sitting and cheerfully refilled our glasses with cold unsweetened tea.

While we were reminiscing, Tim began singing an old song by Melanie Safka. "I ride my bike, I roller skate, don't drive no car…"

We all joined him in singing that little ditty. We were making new memories.

Smiling at that thought, I continued. But Tim, the story didn't end there. The next day Dad told Lois and me that he wanted to take us into town. He got into his pick-up truck and motioned for us to join him. Our quiet twenty-minute ride seemed like an eternity.

Dad parked in front of Sailor's Bike shop that sold Schwinn Bikes. He usually didn't show much emotion, but at that moment he looked as though he had won the sweepstakes from Publishers Clearing House. Maybe he had, or maybe he sold a lot of strawberries. It didn't matter to us because he told us that he wanted to buy us both a new bike. Lois and I looked at each other wide-eyed with excitement, squealed with glee, as we jumped out of the truck. As we entered the shop, Lois went her way and I went mine. It didn't take long to pick out our very own brand, new bikes! I chose the most beautiful shade of purple with two white stripes on the front and back fender. At the end of the shiny silver handlebars were purple and white tassels.

Lois blurted out after a mouthful of strawberry pie. "And mine was light green with two pinstripes on the fender with a shiny rack on the rear!"

Tim chuckled, "I bet they were girl's bikes with no crossbar."

In unison, Lois and I replied, "Yup!" The ride home was nothing like the quiet ride there. We couldn't stop talking about the adventures we were going to have!

Once we arrived home, we took our bikes from the back of

the pick-up and raced them to the house to show our mom who had just got home from work. She greeted us with big hugs and said, "Show me how you ride." Lois and I rode around the yard, then raced down the path to our grandparents, who were sitting on their steps clapping for us. Grandma handed Lois a brown paper sack of homemade molasses cookies for our family.

Tim teared up, "I feel like I was there!" I was taken back for a moment as I could just taste those moist and delicious cookies with that one plump raisin in the middle. Tim stood up, stretched and asked with a grin, "Why didn't Martha, Kathy and Pam get a new bike and where was Thelma, our youngest sister?"

Martha responded in her soft, gentle voice "Thelma was just a baby. I loved taking care of her while the rest of you guys played."

Kathy added, "I enjoyed pulling Pam around in our little red Radio Flyer wagon."

Pam blurted out, "I got my bike later!"

"Oh sis," Tim cried, "Thank you for sharing this great story. I miss our parents and all of the family members who have passed away."

All of us stood up, huddled in a circle hugging each other tight as Misty, Roger's daughter snuck up on us and hollered, "Everyone say cheese" as she snapped a picture. It was a picture perfect memory with sibling love from our Heavenly Father from above.

I will always hold onto the joy that my dad felt by making his little girls happy that day. It must have meant so much to him to take my sister and I shopping to pick out our very first bikes. Not only did he take the time, but he must have saved money for quite a while. I thank God for special memories.

If you enjoyed Summer in the Mitten,
then you are sure to like

Available on Amazon

SHIAWASSEE
Area Writers

Find us on Facebook @ shiareawriters for other locations, appearances, and meeting dates.

Made in the USA
Columbia, SC
30 May 2021